12-00

MICHAEL RYGOL

CAD
for
VLSI

CAD
for
VLSI

G. Russell (editor)
D.J. Kinniment
E.G. Chester
M.R. McLauchlan

University of Newcastle upon Tyne

 Van Nostrand Reinhold (UK) Co. Ltd

First published in 1985 by
Van Nostrand Reinhold (UK) Co. Ltd
Molly Millars Lane, Wokingham, Berkshire, England

Typeset in Times 10 on 11pt by
Columns Ltd, Reading

Printed in Great Britain by J.W. Arrowsmith Ltd, Bristol

British Library Cataloguing in Publication Data

CAD for VLSI.
   1. Integrated circuits—Very large scale
   integration—Data processing
   I. Russell, G.
   621.381'73   TK7874

ISBN 0-442-30618-0

Contents

Preface

It has long been accepted that, to exploit fully the capabilities of microelectronic technology, it is essential to establish a synergism between man and computer in the IC design process. Over the past quarter of a century a vast number of technical papers have been published on the use of computers in all aspects of the design of integrated circuits; this information, however, is dispersed throughout many journals and technical papers, requiring designers to perform an extensive literature search to gain an overview of CAD techniques for IC design. Since the advent of VLSI, there has been an explosive growth in the number of CAD techniques which have evolved to overcome the major issue in the design of integrated circuits — namely, complexity. It was thus considered timely to produce an overview, in a single volume, of the use of computers in the different phases of the IC design process.

The contents of this book are based on a course given jointly by the Department of Electrical and Electronic Engineering and the Computing Laboratory, University of Newcastle upon Tyne, over the past three years to leading semiconductor and computer manufacturing companies. Those present at these courses ranged from managers and experienced designers to graduates embarking on a career in the microelectronics industry. The material has been presented in this book in such a way that undergraduate and postgraduate students, on courses in CAD techniques for integrated circuit design, will find it ideally suited to their needs.

Chapter 1 is a brief review of the development of CAD techniques over the past 30 years and looks at future trends.

Since the development of CAD tools is strongly influenced by changes in technology and design methodologies, the next two chapters discuss various design problems and layout styles. For many designers, their association with CAD will be from the end users perspective; hence Chapter 4 describes a typical CAD system. Chapter 5 describes a design style using PLAs, which can be supported by a simple set of design tools and has therefore found wide acceptance in universities as a means of designing relatively complex integrated circuits.

Chapters 6–11 discuss the current collection of CAD tools, each chapter being dedicated to a particular CAD tool: for example, simulation, test pattern generation, automatic layout, and so on.

Chapter 12 discusses the use of high-level description languages and emphasizes the importance of describing systems at high levels of abstraction to overcome the problems of complexity. The final chapter is also concerned with languages in design and introduces the concept of functional programming languages and their application to the specification of digital systems.

G.R.
D.J.K.
E.G.C.
M.R.McL.

Acknowledgements

The authors wish to acknowledge, first, their appreciation to Plessey Research (Caswell) for permission to publish this book, which is based on the material presented as a series of lectures on CAD to the company; second, the individual contributions made by the personnel from the company; in particular, Mr C. Wiseman, who initiated the idea of presenting the series of lectures upon which this book is based, and also Mr J. Dickson for his constructive criticisms about the contents of the course, based on the comments of those present at the course.

Finally, the authors wish to thank Ailsa Moore and Jonette Cowen, TYPEX, who had the unenviable task of deciphering the hieroglyphics of the authors in the preparation of the draft manuscript of this text.

1 Introduction

1.1 CAD — an evolutionary discipline [1]–[4]

The concept of using computers to assist in the design of digital systems was conceived in the mid-1950s. The impetus to develop CAD tools was strongly influenced by the introduction of the transistor as a switching device in digital circuits. The transistor, although promising the realization of more compact and faster computer systems, introduced several design problems which, due to their complexity, were not amenable to solution by manual design methods; consequently computers had to be used in the design process to resolve these problems. Furthermore, the advantages offered by this second generation of computer systems attracted a greater demand from customers, and in order to satisfy delivery schedules computers were also introduced into the manufacturing process.

The first applications of computers in the design process were concerned with the generation and updating of the logic diagrams, now stored on magnetic tape reels as text files; these could be edited easily and new versions of the diagrams produced on the line printer. Computers were also used to design the wiring layout of the 'logic-drawers' into which the printed circuit boards, realizing the basic logic functions, were inserted. Computers were used in this part of the design process to determine the interconnection paths of the wires in the logic-drawers, so as to minimize the amount of noise pick-up between wires, to which transistors were very susceptible. The information relating to interconnection routes was later passed to automatic wire-wrap machines which then implemented the physical interconnections on the logic drawers; this automatic manufacturing step eliminated a vast amount of checking which had to be performed, on *each* drawer, when the interconnections were routed manually.

However, with the use of automatic manufacturing tools it was essential that the input data to these machines were correct, consequently a suite of data-integrity checking programs evolved which ensured that, first, the interconnection data did not contain net lists which would exceed the fan-out drive capability of the gates on the printed circuit boards; second, two boards had not been assigned to the same slot on the logic-drawer; third, a given pin on the logic-drawer did not have more than three wire wraps.

Now that it could be ensured that the interconnections of the functions on the logic-drawers were correct, the question which remained to be answered was whether or not the complex Boolean expressions realized by the logic-drawers performed the function intended by the designer. To answer this question logic level simulators were developed which enabled designers to verify the functions realized by sets of Boolean expressions. The designers now had a suite of programs which would enable them to verify their designs and ensure that their implementation in hardware was correct. The information required to implement a given Boolean expression, that is gate types and interconnections, could also be generated automatically from the Boolean expressions used in the simulator, thus ensuring a consistency in the data used in the simulation and physical implementation of the Boolean expressions.

It was soon discovered that the complexity of the problems evolving in the design of digital systems was exceeding the capabilities of the computers, particularly the problem of logic simulation, which required a vast amount of data storage; a partial solution to this problem was found by partitioning the system into smaller subfunctions and then simulating these in turn. This solution, however, was not wholly satisfactory, since it incurred long simulation times, which was further aggravated by limited access to the host computer as it was used by other departments in the company for basic data processing tasks. In attempts to overcome the simulation problem, CAD tools were developed which could be used at a higher level of abstraction with subsequent automatic synthesis into gate level functions; however, this approach resulted in designs which contained two to three times as many components as necessary.

The problems with the CAD tools ultimately affected the short production schedules envisaged by management, who had been completely overwhelmed by the potential offered by introducing computers into the design process. The problem of extended production schedules was further compounded by the designers who, dissatisfied by the performance of the CAD tools, reverted to manual design techniques, in many cases against management directives. However, it was soon accepted, although reluctantly by management, that the current performance of computer systems was inadequate, in general, for the solution of the complex problems which occurred in the design of digital systems in a production environment. Subsequently research and development into the use of CAD tools over the next decade was continued only in universities or companies which had a large research budget.

In the early 1970s a renewed interest evolved in the use of CAD techniques in the design of digital systems. This interest was partly initiated, again, by changes in technology, namely, the integrated circuit and the problems which evolved in their design. At this time the design of integrated circuit layouts, using manual methods, was becoming impractical due to their complexity; consequently other design methods were sought. The introduction of interactive computer graphics systems provided the solution to this problem; descriptions of sections of a layout could be input to the graphics systems from a digitizer, whereupon modifications could be easily made to the layout, which could then be added to other parts of the layout already in the system. The output from the graphics system could either be large check plots for visual inspection or the drive tapes for various types of mask-making equipment.

These design tools were readily accepted by the design engineers who could see their obvious benefits over existing manual design techniques. In addition to this revived interest in using CAD tools, many designers began to develop their own tools and throughout the 1970s a plethora of layout design tools developed for performing dimension rule checking, connectivity checking, layout-to-logic consistency checking, etc. Also, with the introduction of integrated circuits a third generation of computers evolved with better performance characteristics in terms of storage capacity and computational speed; consequently, interest was revived in simulation techniques at all levels of abstraction and other computationally intensive programs were developed, for example automatic test generation programs and fault simulators.

In the late 1970s further developments in CAD tools were required due to circuit complexities exceeding the capabilities of the tools, as a result, again, of the advances in semiconductor device technology. At this time the CAD tools, in general, considered the integrated circuit as a monolithic entity without any structure and consequently their capabilities were easily exceeded by the vast amount of data which was to be processed. To overcome this complexity problem the next generation of CAD tools had to impose a design methodology upon the user; this approach was considered revolutionary, since, in the past, acceptance of CAD tools into a design process had been incremental and oriented towards pseudo-manual design styles. The first stage in this revolution was the introduction of a design style such that the CAD tools could capitalize on the regularity and repetitivity of the functions in the circuit, for example, RAMs, ROMs and shift registers. Simple design languages were developed to describe the layout of these functions at a high level, from which detailed layout information at mask level could be generated automatically. In some instances the layout of a function, for example the PLA, could be generated from its logical specification. Since designers were now thinking in terms of functions much more complex than primitive gates, there was a need to develop high-level simulation tools, which also improved the simulation efficiency of large circuits. Low-level mask-verification tools — for example, design rule checkers — were also modified to take advantage of the structure in the circuit, making them more efficient. The amount of low-level checking required in layout design was also greatly reduced by the introduction of symbolic layout methods with automatic compaction to predefined design rules which subsequently produced error-free designs.

The present trend in CAD design tools is towards complete design automation with the objective of decreasing design times by removing many of the detailed design decisions from the designer, at the expense, however, of increased silicon area or reduced performance. It may be considered that the first step towards complete chip design automation was the introduction of the PLA generator. On a larger scale, such tools as data path generators and silicon compilers, which translate a high-level description of the system into a layout level description, are being developed to produce complete systems; however, few CAD tools of this type exist, at present, in a production environment.

1.2   The design process and associated CAD tools [5]–[11]

The overall design process is characterized by a series of transformations of a high-level specification of a system, through several levels of abstraction, to its physical realization. The levels of abstraction in the design process can be categorized, broadly, as architectural level, behavioural level, functional level, gate level, circuit level and layout level. It should be noted that above functional level, the levels of abstraction are not well defined, with behavioural level being replaced in some instances by instruction level, algorithmic level or register transfer level; however, the common theme about these levels of abstraction is that they define the behaviour of the system with little or no reference to its physical structure.

At architectural level the designer's main interest is the overall structure of the system, which is usually described in terms of high-level primitives such as processors, memories and I/O devices, the primitives being characterized by parameters such as memory capacity, access times, word lengths, data transmission rates, processor performance etc.

At this level the designer is also interested in the global data flow between the high-level primitives in the system with the objective of estimating the system performance and identifying potential bottle-necks in the data transmission within the system. The CAD tools which the designer has at his disposal for these purposes are systems level simulators, e.g. GPSS, which permit him to observe the global behaviour of the system. With LSI designs this level of simulation was rarely used; however, since the advent of VLSI and the implementation of complex digital systems, for example the *transputer*, on a single chip, systems level simulators will be used more often in the integrated circuit design process.

At behavioural level a procedural description of the function of each of the above high-level primitives is produced without any specific reference to their final implementation, each high-level primitive being considered as an autonomous subsystem. Recently, a proliferation of behavioural/hardware description languages has evolved: for example, FML, HILO and ELLA, to describe the function of high-level primitives. Associated with these description languages there is also a simulator so that the functions described by the language can be verified.

At functional level each of the subsystems is described, where possible, as a collection of defined functional blocks — for example, RAMs, ALUs, PLAs, shift registers etc. — which will be used to realize the behaviour of the subsystem described by the hardware description languages. At this level of the design process the designer is becoming more interested in the timing relationships of signals between the functional blocks within the subsystem. The timing relationships between the signals and the general interaction of the functional blocks is established using a functional level simulator, e.g. FLOGIC, HILO. Attempts have also been made to perform automatic test pattern generation and fault simulation functions at this level, in order to reduce the complexity of the problem of performing these tasks at lower levels of abstraction.

At gate level individual functions are realized as connections of basic switching and storage elements. The designer is now concerned with the logical behaviour of the functional blocks: signal transitions are described using three or more values; various delays are assigned to the elements in the functional blocks — for example, rise and fall times, propagation delays, set up and hold times. In addition to verifying the logical behaviour of the function by using a gate level simulator, the designer may also use the simulator to flag switching anomalies which are present in the circuit. Other CAD tools used extensively at gate level are automatic test generation programs which derive sets of input test patterns to detect a given class of logical faults in the circuit; the fault coverage of these patterns is usually determined by using a fault simulator. The cost of performing test pattern generation and fault simulation grows rapidly with circuit complexity; in attempts to reduce these costs testability analysis programs have been developed which determine, without the use of test generation or simulation, how difficult it will be to test a given circuit, enabling the designer to identify parts of the circuit which need to be altered in order to ease the testing process and hence reduce testing costs.

At circuit level individual gates or small groups of switching elements are represented by groups of transistors whose analogue function is determined by a circuit level simulator. The circuit characteristics of interest at this level of the design process are accurate predictions of rise and fall times, propagation delays, loading effects, etc.

Recently, two additional levels of simulation have been introduced which overlap gate and circuit levels of abstraction in the design process: the first is called *timing simulation*, which is essentially a relaxed form of circuit simulation and can be used efficiently to simulate the analogue performance of large digital circuits; the second is called *switch level*, where the transistors in the circuit are represented by switches and a logic level simulation is performed on the circuit, whose description has been derived directly from the layout.

During the design process situations occur where it is required to obtain a detailed simulation of a small part of a circuit whilst maintaining its relationship to the environment. In the past this would require the complete circuit to be described at the given level of abstraction, which in the case of circuit level would result in extended and expensive simulation runs. To overcome this difficulty the concept of 'mixed-mode' simulation was introduced, to permit sections of a circuit to be described at whatever level of abstraction is most applicable and thereafter perform a concurrent simulation of each section at the appropriate level. At present, mixed-mode simulators are generally available which embrace circuit, timing and gate levels of abstraction; however, some mixed-mode simulators have been developed which include the higher levels of abstraction — for example, functional level.

The design process is characterized by the top-down decomposition of the system into basic cells followed by a bottom-up implementation, the basic cells being interconnected to form macro cells, which in turn are combined to form subfunctions and so on until the complete system has been implemented.

In the past the basic cells were designed manually by sketching the layout on quadrille paper and thereafter entering a description of the cells into the computer using a digitizer or by using a special purpose layout description language which defined the shapes, their mask levels and coordinates; the cell layout could then be modified using interactive graphics. More recently, however, basic cell design has been made more efficient by using symbolic layout techniques. This enables transistors, contacts and interconnections to be represented by symbols which are subsequently replaced by the necessary geometries to realize these functions on the layout. Symbolic layout methods can be either static or dynamic; in the static method the symbols are placed on a fixed grid, the designer being responsible for complying to the layout design rules, on the other hand with the dynamic method the symbols are only placed in relative positions, and after they have been replaced by the appropriate mask geometries they are automatically compacted in accordance with some set of predefined layout rules; in this way basic cell design can be performed very efficiently.

After the basic cells have been designed, the detail is abstracted from the cells which are subsequently represented by a 'bounding box' with pins located around the periphery to identify the interconnect points to the cell for inputs/outputs, power and ground. In some instances the cell descriptions are converted into a layout language format; the descriptions are subsequently considered to be procedures to which parameters may be passed when they are embedded in a high-level programming language which provides a mechanism to generate the layout of larger functional blocks comprising many instances of the basic cells arranged in a regular pattern.

In composing larger functions from several subfunctions, automatic layout programs are used to place and route the interconnections to the subfunctions, the interconnections being made on one or more layers depending upon the complexity of the fabrication process used to manufacture the circuit. However, if silicon area is an important design criterion the layout may be done manually, since automatic techniques tend to increase chip size.

When manual methods are used in layout design, the layout must be checked for errors — for example, design rule violations, logic functions with missing inputs or outputs, incorrectly connected functions, etc. — consequently a range of tools, referred to as topological analysis tools, have been developed to detect these types of errors in the layout. The most widely used topological analysis tool is probably the *design rule checker*, which ensures that the dimensions of the shapes and their relationship with other shapes in the layout comply with predefined values which, for a given fabrication process, produce an acceptable yield. Also, when manual layout methods are used the designer must ensure that the layout realizes the intended logic function of the circuit. In deriving the function of the circuit from the layout, the designer must first identify the transistors in the layout, second establish the logic gate function realized by groups of transistors, third establish the interconnectivity between logic gates and finally check the reconstructed circuit against the circuit description used at the gate level simulation phase in the design process. CAD tools have been developed for each stage in the reconstruction process; however, efficient methods of comparing the reconstructed and reference circuits are still active areas for research.

The amount of topological analysis which must be performed on a layout is dependent upon the amount of manual intervention. However, with design tools and methodologies which guarantee 'correctness by construction' the amount of checking performed on layouts will be greatly reduced in the future.

1.3 Future trends in CAD tools [12]–[14]

It is well known that predicted chip complexities far exceed the capabilities of present-day CAD systems to produce VLSI circuits within a competitive time scale of say, six man months. Consequently a topic which is continually discussed is whether or not current philosophies towards the development of CAD tools is correct.

Two basic philosophies exist, the first of which is directed towards the complete design automation system and the second towards the design assistant, which implies a degree of interaction between the designer and the computer system. The advantages of a complete design automation system is that design times will be shorter, because of the constrained design environment with enforced design rules which will result, ideally, in error free designs; the main disadvantage of these systems, however, is the excessive use of silicon area for the implementation of the design. The design assistant, on the other hand, permits the designer to make decisions about global issues, whilst it concerns itself with local issues and implementation details. In this instance high-density designs can be produced with a corresponding increase in design time. The decision as to which philosophy to adopt depends upon the end product of the design: for example, computer manufacturers would probably adopt the complete design automation system, since in this environment design times are more important than the cost of larger circuits, which is insignificant in comparison to the cost of the complete system. However, companies whose end products are integrated circuits are more interested in silicon area; consequently they would adopt the design assistant philosophy.

However, regardless of the particular philosophy adopted, the main objective of the CAD system is, in the first instance, to reduce the number of design errors, consequently the emphasis on the function of CAD tools, particularly at layout level, has moved from one of analysis to synthesis: for example, the PLA generator produces a layout description directly from its functional specification, and the complete artwork may be generated for cell designs described initially in a symbolic format such as STICKS. Furthermore, whereas in the past CAD tools performed analysis of the complete circuit, which it considered as a monolithic entity, these tools have now been redesigned to make use of the structure in the design and have subsequently become more efficient. However, the use of more synthesis tools in the design process will soon render the use of analysis tools obsolete.

1.3.1 SPECIAL PURPOSE CAD HARDWARE [15]–[17]

The increase in complexity of VLSI circuits demands an increase in the efficiency of CAD tools. This efficiency is currently limited by the use of computers which have a general purpose architecture as the host machine for the CAD tools. In order to overcome this efficiency barrier, special purpose architectures are being designed which exploit the parallelism and concurrency which exists in most CAD algorithms. The increase in efficiency of these special purpose architectures reduces design times and also permits a more detailed analysis to be performed on the designs which, due to the computational intensity of the task, was previously limited only to small designs. The cost of these special purpose architectures, which may comprise two to three hundred ICs, is very much less than the cost of the software to do a similar task. Although these special purpose architectures offer several advantages they also have several limitations: for example, the specialized nature of the hardware limits its use — architectures used for simulation cannot be readily adapted for routing or dimension rule checking; furthermore, the special purpose architectures require a host computer not only to translate the description of a circuit into a format acceptable to the special purpose architecture but also to transfer this data to it and receive the results from it.

Consequently, if the amount of translation and data transmission time is large in comparison to computational complexity of a given problem the performance of the special purpose architecture can be slower than a general purpose computer performing the same task.

At present special purpose architectures have been designed to perform simulation, test pattern generation, testability analysis, routing and placement and design rule checking, although few systems are commercially available. The increase in performance of these tools is effected by dividing a given algorithm between several processors, each one being dedicated, essentially, to a subroutine in the algorithm; furthermore, a large amount of parallel processing is also implemented in these structures which, in the case of gate level simulation, for example, permits gate changes which occur at the same time to be simulated concurrently, a task which cannot be implemented in a software gate level simulator.

The continual increase in design complexities together with the reduction of hardware costs tends to favour the continued development of specialized hardware for CAD tools; this is offset, however by the introduction of more powerful general purpose machines, and by improved algorithms and design methodologies aimed at combating complexity elegantly rather than by sheer computational power. Although both approaches have distinct advantages and may be seen in opposition to each other, it is considered that if a system is designed which incorporates the merits of both approaches, then a vastly superior CAD system will be produced.

1.3.2 SILICON COMPILERS AND ASSEMBLERS [18]–[22]

The VLSI design process is a combination of top-down decomposition of the system into more complex subsystems with a bottom-up implementation. Bottom-up implementation comprises assembling higher-level functions from lower-level primitives or subfunctions. However, errors can readily occur in this composition process which are not detected until late in the design cycle when they are more costly to correct. In an attempt to improve this part of the design process a class of CAD tool, called the silicon compiler, has evolved whose philosophy to the error free implementation of a function is 'correctness by construction'.

The objective of the silicon compiler is to translate a high-level behavioural specification of a system into a layout level description of the system in a given target architecture. Examples of silicon compilers developed to date are Bristle Blocks, whose target system architecture is the data path comprising data processing blocks interconnected by data busses, and the FIRST system used to design signal processing circuits configured in a bit serial architecture; attempts have also been made to develop silicon compilers which do not constrain the designer to a given architecture. In the absence of the 'ideal' system an interim solution has been found in the *IC module compiler*, which produces specific blocks in an IC layout, the block description being generated from parameterized cells; these blocks must then be interconnected either manually or by using autolayout programs.

The *chip assembler* is another tool which has been developed to assist in the design of IC layouts. It is essentially a data management tool whose function is to collect, manipulate and store all the data associated with a design. The chip assembler differs from the silicon compiler in two aspects; first it does not impose a target architecture on the designer, except that it must be hierarchical; and second there is a considerable amount of man–machine interaction, since the silicon assembler provides an environment in which conventional CAD tools can be integrated. In designing with the silicon assembler the system is considered to comprise a series of rectangular functional blocks which are used to construct a floor plan of the layout; the interface connections between the blocks are either made by direct abutment, stretch and abut or a simple river route connection. The design of each block is subsequently refined until the lowest-level primitives are reached, which may be library cells, parameterized functional blocks or hand-crafted cells. During the design process the most important function performed by the assembler is the management of the functional block interface specifications, since it is normal practice to partition the design task among several designers who work independently; hence it is essential to ensure that the interface specifications are adhered to. In the event of an interface specification being violated, the effect on adjacent blocks can readily be assessed and a decision made whether to change the specification or insist that the block causing the violation is redesigned to suit the specification. Also, within the chip assembler, where possible the same functional and structural hierarchies are maintained, since this approach reduces the amount of checking to be performed if a given element in either hierarchy is to be modified. The chip assembler also provides automatic documentation on a design together with a mechanism for monitoring the progress of the design of the component parts of a system so that, if required, more design effort may be directed to the problem area.

1.3.3 EXPERT SYSTEMS FOR INTEGRATED CIRCUIT DESIGN [23]–[25]

Recently, there has evolved a growing community interested in implementing systems on silicon, but to whom the design process appears to be a 'black art' and who require the assistance of an expert when certain design decisions have to be made; this assistance, however, cannot be obtained from the present range of CAD tools, which are passive in nature. Consequently there is a requirement for a design system which can essentially 'think' and have the knowledge base of an expert so that when design decisions have to be made there is an expert knowledge base which can be interrogated to obtain an answer.

An expert system is a knowledge-intensive program capable of providing solutions to a range of non-numerical problems which in the past required the knowledge of a human expert to provide the solution. An expert system comprises a knowledge base together with some inference mechanism to manipulate or interrogate the knowledge base and hence perform the 'reasoning' function associated with expert systems. The knowledge base comprises a series of 'antecedent–consequent' rules of the form of IF (condition) THEN (action). These rules form part of an inference net which enable certain deductions to be made from given input data; it is also possible to interrogate the expert system to obtain the 'thought path' followed by the system through the inference net in coming to a given conclusion.

Since expert systems, when solving problems, essentially manipulate symbols which represent objects and their relationships, recourse had to be made to a class of programming languages called *logic programming languages*, of which PROLOG is the most popular to date. A PROLOG program comprise three parts: first, a declaration of facts about objects and their relationships in the problem to be solved; second, the definition of a set of rules about these objects and their relationships; and finally a mechanism for determining the consequences of these relationships or their validity.

PROLOG has been used to implement several CAD programs such as simulators and automatic test generation programs; however, it offered no advantage over existing implementations of these programs using algorithmic languages, because these particular types of program produce results through numerical computation rather than deduction. In the design process PROLOG is more suited to design verification problems such as checking the integrity of the description of a function at different levels of abstraction or ensuring that a circuit conforms to a set of design rules which will enhance its testability. In general, however, the use of expert systems in the design of integrated circuits is still in its infancy, although advanced experts systems do exist in other disciplines.

References

1. Breuer, M.A. *Design Automation of Digital Systems*: Vol. 1, *Theory and Techniques*. Prentice-Hall (1972), pp. 1–19.
2. Barbe, D.F. *Very Large Scale Integration, VLSI: Fundamentals and Applications*. Springer-Verlag (1980), pp. 89–127.
3. Negrete, M.R. Viewpoints — Macro Negrete on structured VLSI design. *Hewlett-Packard Journal*, **32**(6), 3–4 (1981).
4. Feuer, M. VLSI design automation: an introduction. *Proc. IEEE*, **71**(1), 5–9 (1983).
5. Trimberger, S. *et al.* A structured design methodology and associated software tools. *IEEE Trans. Circuits and Systems*, **CAS-28**(7), 618–33 (1981).
6. Director, S.W., *et al.* A design methodology and computer aids for digital VLSI systems. *IEEE Trans. Circuits and Systems*, **CAS-28**(7), 634–5 (1981).
7. Allen, J. and Penfield, P. VLSI design automation activities at MIT. *IEEE Trans. Circuits and Systems*, **CAS-28**(7), 645–53 (1981).
8. Dutton, R.W. Stanford overview in VLSI research. *IEEE Trans. Circuits and Systems*, **CAS-28**(7), 654–65 (1981).
9. Daniel, M.E. and Gwyn, C.W. CAD systems for IC design. *IEEE Trans. Computer Aided Design of Integrated Circuits and Systems*, **CAD-1**(1), 2–12 (1982).
10. Van Cleemput, W.M. CAD tools for custom integrated circuit design. *Digest of Papers Compcon '82*, 259–62 (Spring 1982).
11. Niessen, C. Hierarchical design methodologies and tools for VLSI chips. *Proc. IEEE*, **71**(1), 66–75 (1983).
12. Gibson, D. Panel discussion: can CAD meet the VLSI design problems of the 80's. *Proc. 16th Design Automation Conference*, 543–53 (1979).
13. Rosenberg, L.M. The evolution of design automation to meet the challenges of VLSI. *Proc. 17th Design Automation Conference*, 3–11 (1980).
14. McCaw, C.R. Panel discussion: design automation and VLSI in the 80s. *Proc. 17th Design Automation Conference*, 336–47 (1980).
15. Adshead, H.G. Towards VLSI complexity: the DA algorithm scaling problem — can special DA hardware help?. *Proc. 19th Design Automation Conference* 339–44 (1982).

16. Blank, T. A survey of hardware accelerators used in computer aided design. *IEEE Design and Test of Computers*, 21–39 (August 1984).

17. Howard, J.K., Malm, R.L. and Warren, L.M. Introduction to the IBM Los Gatos Logic Simulation Machine. *Proc. IEEE International Conference on Computer Design: VLSI in Computers* 580–3 (October 1983).

18. Mudge, J.C., *et al*. A VLSI chip assembler. *Design Methodologies for Very Large Scale Integrated Circuits*, NATO Advanced Summer Institute, Belgium (1980).

19. Rupp, C.R. The components of a silicon compiler system. *VLSI '81*, Academic Press, 227–36 (1981).

20. Werner, J. The silicon compiler: panacea, wishful thinking or old hat. *VLSI Design*, 46–53 (September/October 1982).

21. Katz, H.R. and Weiss, S. Chip assemblers: concepts and capabilities. *Proc. 20th Design Automation Conference*, 25–30 (June 1983).

22. Elias, N.J. and Wetzel, E.W. The IC module compiler: a VLSI system design aid. *Proc. 20th Design Automation Conference*, 46–9 (June 1983).

23. Horstmann, P.W. Expert systems and logic programming for CAD. *VLSI Design*, 37–46 (November 1983).

24. Shrobe, H.E. AI meets CAD. *VLSI '83, VLSI Design of Digital Systems*, Elsevier Science Publishers (1983), pp. 387–99.

25. Hayes-Roth, F. A knowledge based expert system: a tutorial. *Computer*, 11–28 (September 1984).

2 Technology and design

2.1 Introduction

Integrated circuit (IC) design as a skill somewhat distinct from discrete circuit design has been with us since the invention of the first monolithic integrated circuit before 1960, and at that time what made it different from the traditional circuit design techniques was a need to take into account the characteristics of the medium in the design of the circuit.

An understanding was needed of different relative costs of components. Transistors were no longer high-cost devices when compared with resistors, and economies could be made in area by using transistors with a common isolation area, e.g. common collector bipolar transistors. A knowledge of the underlying physics of the devices and their interaction with the surface geometry was needed to appreciate the variation in characteristics available within a reasonable area, and ideas of matched devices on a single chip led to new circuit concepts such as the current mirror.

These skills are still required in the design of the much more complex chips of the 1980s and 1990s, but where in the past IC design could be done with a few additions to the mental tool kit of the average physicist or electronic engineer the range of disciplines needed is now becoming much greater and the emphasis is moving away from an understanding of the physics of the device and towards familiarity with the tools and techniques used by the mathematician and computer scientist in handling complex systems. In the same way that the medium affected the style of circuit design in the 1960s and 1970s it is likely that the characteristics of the medium at a higher level and the tools used to manage the design at the higher level will affect the style of design. This is the area of design methodology.

Chips of around 10^6 transistors are now being produced, and the term very large scale integration (VLSI) is used for the technology required to produce them.

The initials VLSI are often used by different people in contexts with different implications, and two possible definitions of the term are given in Table 2.1. The trend in increasing complexity is illustrated by the maximum

Table 2.1

Date	*a* Linear size of chip (μm)	*b* Minimum line width (μm)	$(a/b)^2 \div 50$ Transistors per chip
1960	1 000	30 μ	22
1970	2 500	10 μ	1 250
1980	6 000	3 μ	80 000
*			
1990	10 000	0.5 μ	8 000 000

* < 2 μm line widths: the point at which complexity overwhelms all other problems.

chip size, *a* μm, and the minimum line width, *b* μm, which could be fabricated in production in a given year.

Assuming a transistor can be fabricated in a silicon area of 50 squares each having a side equal to the minimum line width, the maximum number of transistors on a chip is given by $(a/b)^2 \div 50$.

This kind of calculation pays a great deal of attention to the lithographic dimensions of the chip and the improvement of the process in terms of numbers of transistors, but almost none to whether it is possible to create a useful design with that number of transistors, or the scale of the design task needed to do it.

One way of looking at the difference between LSI and VLSI is from the point of view of the process line engineer who sees the difficulty and cost of reducing line widths to under 2 μm, and the other is from the point of view of the system design engineer who sees the cost and difficulty of creating many new designs on the process provided for him. Since there will be very many more chip designs than processes, and more VLSI system design engineers than process line engineers, the problem of design complexity must be taken seriously.

The cost of design is an increasing proportion of each new chip type because the cost per transistor fabricated has decreased, whilst the cost per transistor designed has remained roughly constant despite increasing use of computer aided design methods. There are several reasons why VLSI design is difficult, as compared with the design of discrete component or software systems, and they include the following.

(1) Very long iteration time for the effect of a minor design change to be seen in a finished chip. This means that designs have to be made as near correct first time as possible.

(2) Poor observability of detailed parts of the design, e.g. the effects of the size of a transistor on the rise time of a bus line.
   Why a particular chip does not meet the required specification may have to be guessed at or deduced from indirect evidence.

(3) A high degree of interaction between different parts of the design, and different aspects of the same part.
   Changes in the size and shape of one component may require a

change in a neighbour, and also the rise time of signals between the two may be affected by the design of both.

(4) A greater need to provide easy testability in an environment where faulty systems are likely to be produced.

2.2 The problem of complexity

Most of these difficulties are related to the design of very complex systems, and if it is possible to reduce the complexity of the system being designed without altering its performance, it may be possible to reduce the design time.

There is often a trade-off between the reduction of design cost by reduction of complexity and increase in fabrication cost by increase in area, but not always, and in a situation where the design cost forms the major proportion it is important to know how these may be traded. In Fig. 2.1 the layout of a chip with five components is shown, in two different versions. In the left-hand version, the components interact in a complex way, so that in changing component (a) there will be not one but several design tasks:

(1) the design of (a);
(2) redesign of (b) to fit with (a);
(3) redesign of (c) to fit with (a).

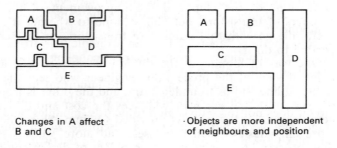

Changes in A affect
B and C

·Objects are more independent
of neighbours and position

Fig. 2.1

This does not take into account any possible knock-on effects to (d) and (e), and also ignores the difficulty of altering the shape of (b) to fit with the new (a). Suppose this were not possible. It is necessary to go back to (a), try another shape, come back to (b) and see if a viable design can now be produced. Iterations of this nature clearly need to be contained.

2.2.1 WHAT IS COMPLEXITY?

As yet there is no formal measure of complexity and the proceding example deals only with one aspect, topology. In a VLSI design components interact in many different ways including at least the following:

(1) layout topology (geometry);
(2) interconnection structure;
(3) timing and sequencing of signals;

(4) electrical characteristics (resistance, capacitance, power);
(5) logic function.

All of these can contribute to the complexity, and the total complexity is not simply measured by the number of components on the chip, nor even the number of different components: 'Given the parts and their behaviours, complexity is the difficulty involved in using the relations among the parts to infer the behaviour of the whole.' [1]

Thus whilst it is not difficult to appreciate that a very repetitive structure such as a 16 384-bit memory can be described simply, given a suitable notation for describing repetition, it may still be complex because of the nature of the interaction between its component cells.

2.2.2 COHESION AND COUPLING

Sequin [2] refers to the concepts of cohesion and coupling in measuring complexity.

Cohesion is the degree to which a group of components belong with each other, rather than with the rest of the system. Clearly if components belong together their interactions are more likely to be local, and global interactions external to the group are minimised. If a design is split into cohesive groups, design changes to a component do not have very far-reaching effects.

The *coupling* is a measure of the amount of interaction between components. The smaller the coupling, the less the design of one component affects another. Figure 2.1 is an example of strong geometrical coupling between components. Strong electrical coupling between components such as loading effects are also to be avoided.

Cohesion and coupling in VLSI are important in the task of partitioning a design. Unlike other system packaging methods, the construction of a VLSI circuit does not force division into boards, modules, and MSI chips at an early stage; but good partitioning is a discipline which must be observed if the complexity of the design is not to become overwhelming. The aims in such a partitioning are to select cohesive subgroups of components within the parent group, and to ensure that the interfaces between the components (electrical and geometrical as well as functional) are simple, thereby reducing the coupling.

2.3 Management of complexity

Many of the methods used in design of very complex systems have come from software design, where the capability to produce very large, interactive programs with their consequent reliability and maintenance problems, has been available for some time. The main techniques are discussed in Sections 2.3.1–4.

2.3.1 PARTITIONING AND HIERARCHY

The approach of 'divide and conquer' [3] in which the overall objective is first specified, and then the problem is functionally decomposed into sub-problems.

Decomposition is then recursively applied to the sub-problems until the resulting tasks are sufficiently simple for their solution to be self evident. In hardware terms this usually (though not necessarily) implies a hierarchical chip organisation where a specific area of the chip deals with each of the sub-problems.

Difficulties with this for VLSI are that some aspects of the design (e.g. the silicon area required for solution of a given problem) may not be visible at the chip level, and it is necessary to iterate up and down the design hierarchy to achieve area minimization.

The advantage of a specification at each level — what the hardware is supposed to do, as distinct from the implementation or how it does the job — is that the behaviour of a group of submodules can be verified before detailed design of the submodules themselves.

2.3.2 LIMITATION OF THE NUMBER OF DESIGN TASKS

The more repetitive a design is, and the fewer the total number of different modules that have to be designed, the shorter the design task. Use of a library of predesigned and pretested cells provides a way of reducing the effort, but if new cells have to be created it is important to make them general, and hence usable in many applications.

2.3.3 ABSTRACTION AND SIMPLE INTERFACES

At each level in the design task it is important to keep the number of different ways in which the components can interact to a minimum, and to choose an appropriate and limited set of modes of interaction.

The purpose of abstraction is to hide the lower-level details of a component by a set of simplifying assumptions. This enables the designer to concentrate on the high-level design task, and not be distracted by irrelevant detail. An example of a common abstraction is the idea of digital logic circuits where the detailed operation of the transistors is assembled to conform to a simple Boolean expression.

Keeping the interfaces between components simple and ensuring that the interface rules are obeyed by the components themselves is important also in avoiding the spread of problems. The main reason for the success of digital techniques over analogue methods is the simplicity of the interface between components. The components themselves usually have a lower performance and a higher cost per function than analogue components, but in large systems the tolerance of digital techniques to minor impedance variations, noise and ignorance of the internal operation of each component is an overwhelming advantage which has made the design of large computer systems possible.

Restriction of the number of structuring constructs to a few well-defined types has parallels in software, [4] and again it is important that these constructs be well chosen.

2.3.4 HIGH-LEVEL NOTATION

It is interesting to note that in both hardware and software environments, the design task averages about 10 items per day [5] committed to file, irrespective of whether these items are lines of code, transistors or other kinds of object. This also holds if the description language is geometry or machine code at one extreme or register transfer or high-level language at the other. It therefore pays to design at as high a level as possible, since the productivity will be greater, and to eliminate the bottom level design tasks by the use of a suitable library.

The notation itself is very important since an inappropriate choice can make the design task more difficult rather than less, and here developments in software may also be useful.

Concepts such as parameterization of library cells lead to economies in the number of different types of cell through the design of generic cells, and in the future formal verification may be possible [6] if the semantics of the notation 'are also formal'.

2.4 The place of CAD

Computers can provide considerable assistance in the design process, particularly when a mechanical process is required to translate one representation of a design into another where the mapping is well defined: for example, taking a list of predesigned cells and their position and drawing a detailed diagram of a composite chip.

They are not generally capable of solving problems in which the amount of computation needed increases exponentially with size of the problem, and if a VLSI design is made arbitrarily complex, then a CAD system will be overwhelmed in the same way as a human designer, but at a slightly later stage.

The tools used in the past have developed with the scale of integration, and the evolution is indicated in Table 2.2.

2.4.1 THE 'SILICON COMPILER'

The aim of good CAD tools is to free the designer as much as possible from irrelevant details so that he can concentrate on the creative aspects for a design, and to make use of the power and accuracy of computers in mapping the ideas to the silicon. Software tools already exist which allow algorithms to be expressed in a high-level form, which bears a closer relationship to a set of mathematical statements than to the details of the computer system on which the algorithm is to be executed. The transformation from high-level language to an executable form is done by a compiler, and in the same way it should be possible to provide a 'silicon compiler' able to transform an algorithm expressed in some abstract form into a detailed chip design.

Whilst some partially successful compilers have been written they tend to be restrictive in the architectures they can accommodate and present tools are better described as 'design automation', since they still put the emphasis on the use by a designer of a set of tools such as auto layout, simulation, and design rule checking.

Table 2.2

Design size	CAD tools
Up to 100 transistors	Graphics to handle layout
	Circuit simulation
(Geometrics and device level)	Design rule checking to verify geometry
Up to 80 000 transistors	Predesigned cells of 10–100 transistors produced as above.
	Auto layout methods to connect cell.
(Gate level)	Test pattern generators to check production
	Electrical rule checkers to verify connections
Up to 8 000 000 transistors (system level)	Parameterized libraries of cells
	Hierarchical design methods with proof of correctness between levels
	Correct compilation of designs rather than checking
	Self test
	Technology independence

2.5 Chip architecture

Much of the software which approaches closest to the ideal of a silicon compiler (i.e. it receives an algorithm as input and produces a mask layout as output) achieves this by simplifying the problem at a crucial point. Instead of allowing all possible chip architectures and design methodologies to be explored in order to find the optimum solution, the range of architectures is restricted to a particular floor plan or set of primitive cells. These methods are often sufficiently flexible to solve many design problems with an acceptable cost and performance compromise, but some techniques are very narrow in their range of applications.

The advantages of restricting the possible layout permutations and the primitives available to the compiler are that the mapping can be simple and straightforward, needing to spend little time exploring alternatives, consequently the software is simple to write, and can produce results quickly. The main problems are either that the resulting chips have a relatively large silicon area and a poor performance for a wide range of application, or that they are good over a narrow band of application with very unacceptable results outside that band.

In Fig. 2.2 four commonly used target architectures are shown. This list is by no means exhaustive, but indicates some of the possible alternatives.

(1) The Standard Cell Array
   An array of cells, each of which can be selected by the designer from a predefined library. The design software then chooses the location of the cell and finds the interconnection paths.
(2) The Uncommitted Logic Array (ULA)
   Here the number, locations, and components of all the cells are fixed,

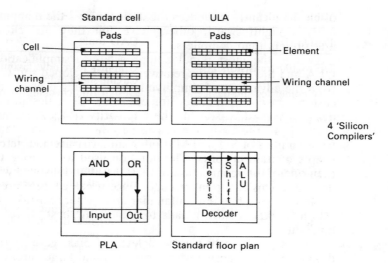

Fig. 2.2

so that transistors and resistors can be prediffused into the silicon. Only interconnection layers differ between designs, and the range of primitive cells available by connecting cell components in different ways is more restricted than in a standard cell array. Again the choice of which primitive cells to use is mainly the responsibility of the designers, but the software chooses the position of the component group required to locate the cell and finds the interconnection paths between cells.

(3) The Programmable Logic Array (PLA)

PLAs rely on the possibility of reducing all combinational logic to minimal sum of products form, and then fitting that sum of products form to a generalized floor plan involving an AND plane to form the set of product terms followed by an OR plane to sum those terms into the required functions. Finite state machines can also be implemented by a simple extension of the floor plan to include a feedback path between outputs and inputs with a state register in that path.

(4) Standard Data Path [7]

Most central processor units in single processing or microprocessor chips require a general mechanism for taking data out of one or more registers, performing logical or arithmetical operations on that data and returning it to a temporary store location in the register block. A simple block diagram of such a data path could include a register block, shifter and ALU each with access to a number of busses to move the data between them. Compilers can be constructed which can compute the number of registers and busses required and decode the operations for a given set of instructions, and they form a useful tool for this restricted range of applications.

Software systems aimed at mechanization of the design process from the system description to set of masks for one of these architectures have sometimes been called silicon compilers, but in fact since the chip architecture often significantly influences the designer, and the mapping process is generally fairly straightforward, others have felt they are closer to assemblers or interpreters than compilers.

Two of the most popular approaches to simplification of the design, the ULA and the PLA, have relatively well-developed software support, and apart from the advantage of simplifying the mapping process, the limited number of customized masks required for each new ULA design minimizes the cost per design. A third reason for the popularity of ULAs is that the primitive cells available to the designers are usually familiar from standard text books and from families of SSI and MSI integrated circuits, i.e. gates, flip flops and other simple digital networks. The notation used to describe the design required is then one of interconnection of these gates and fits well with the thinking of the designer. This is a great strength since it can capture precisely the user's ideas without forcing him into unfamiliar areas where mistakes can be made, but it is also a weakness since it fails to exploit the best characteristics of the silicon medium.

This is particularly true at a level of 5000 gates and above, where many designs make extensive use of registers and larger areas of memory. Mapping all the memory into flip flop cells each of which is mapped onto component groups designed for efficient implementation of NAND gates is not elegant, and in general ULA designs occupy areas about four times larger than the equivalent custom design systems.

Because the chip architecture and methodology for PLAs is so well defined, it is possible, in order to automate the design process, to write software which comes close to the ideal of describing *what* the chip should do rather than *how* it is to do it. Most CAD tools allow a designer to specify his chip in terms of gates or other primitive cells, with the precise electrical connections needed to form the network described in structural detail, if not the actual physical path on the chip. This is essentially *how* the chip should be made, and is usually a refinement of his original concept possibly in the more abstract form of a state diagram for implementation as a finite state machine.

Tools that can capture ideas in this form cut out a stage in the design process which can be error prone, and FSM languages exist which can be completely automatically transformed into PLA architectures. The problem with the use of the PLA as a universal architecture is that digital arithmetic does not map easily into a two-level PLA, and many finite state machines require considerable manipulation before they are realizable in an acceptable area.

2.6 Process scaling and interconnections

Just as the nature of the medium in the past has had an influence on the circuit design, there are characteristics of VLSI technology which may affect the optimum organization of the systems implements. One of the most important of those is that computation (in terms of number of transistors) is likely to be much cheaper than communication (the connections between processing units). The fundamental reasons for this lie in the mechanism for producing more and more transistors on a chip. As the dimensions of devices are reduced laterally, it becomes necessary to reduce vertical dimensions in sympathy in order to allow satisfactory definition of the smaller line widths. Various models of the effects of this scaling of device dimensions can be used to predict the characteristics of submicron devices, and it is not the aim here to discuss the relative merits of different scalings. The results produced by one simple scaling method where the important dimensions of a MOSFET device are reduced from a feature size, λ, of 2.5 μm to 0.25 μm is shown in Fig. 2.3. In this scaling, all dimensiions have been reduced by 10, and all voltages also by 10 to keep the electric fields constant.

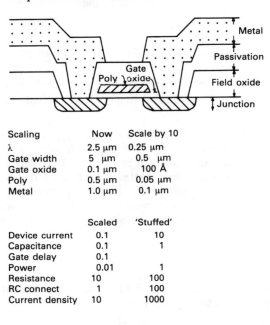

Scaling	Now	Scale by 10
λ	2.5 μm	0.25 μm
Gate width	5 μm	0.5 μm
Gate oxide	0.1 μm	100 Å
Poly	0.5 μm	0.05 μm
Metal	1.0 μm	0.1 μm

	Scaled	'Stuffed'
Device current	0.1	10
Capacitance	0.1	1
Gate delay	0.1	
Power	0.01	1
Resistance	10	100
RC connect	1	100
Current density	10	1000

Fig. 2.3

This causes the currents in the transistors to reduce by a factor of 10, but because conductor areas have reduced by 100, current densities have increased by 10.

If the potential increase by a factor of 100 in number of transistors per chip is used to the full, in other words the chip is 'stuffed' full of components, it becomes clear that the interconnect characteristics become more important.

2.6.1 CONNECTION PERFORMANCE

Because capacitances and voltage swings have decreased, gate delays, which are proportional to CV/I, will fall in the scaled technology. Interconnections on the other hand may still remain as long as in an unscaled chip, because in the 'stuffed' chip it is still necessary to make connections which join one side of the chip to the other. On average, the length of connections does not tend to scale in sympathy with device dimensions and consequently the connection capacitance remains roughly constant. At the same time its resistance increases with reducing cross sectional area, and the product RC increases substantially.

In Table 2.3 these effects are tabulated, and show a change as submicron dimensions are approached and passed, from the familiar world of system

Table 2.3 Interconnection performance

10 mm connection — metal

λ (μλ)	5	2.5	0.5	0.1
R (ohms)	25	100	2500	62 500
C (pF)	4	4	4	4
RC (ps)	100	400	10 00	250 000
Gate (ps)	5	2.5	0.5	0.1

		←	→	
	Performance dominated by circuits		Performance dominated by connections	

Polysilicon connections have approximately 100 × resistance.

performance being dominated by the delay per gate of the technology, to a new one where delays are determined much more by the connections between the gates than the gates themselves. The table assumes that all connections can be made by means of metal patterns and takes the worst case of the 10 mm long path. This may be pessimistic in terms of wire length, but at present many connections are made by conductors with much worse conductivities than metal, for example polysilicon, and they will cause longer delays.

2.6.2 CONNECTION AREA

Not only do the interconnects dominate the performance of a system in VLSI technology, they also dominate the surface of the silicon.

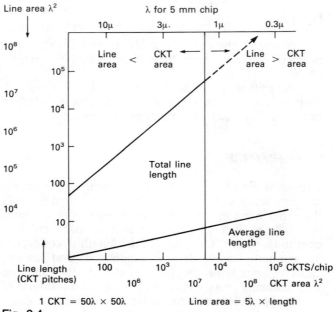

Fig. 2.4

Connection lengths on complex chips remain roughly the same as the device dimensions are reduced, and some research has been done on the relationship between connection length and circuit size in a gate array. This is summarized by 2.4 in which a circuit (or gate) is assumed to take an area of $50\lambda \times 50\lambda$ where λ is the minimum feature size of the technology. As λ reduces from 10 μm to 0.3 μm, the numbers of circuits per chip can be increased from 100 to 100 000 but at the same time the average line length needed to interconnect the circuits goes up from about 2 to 10 circuit pitches. Since the number of the individual interconnects goes up in proportion to the number of circuits the total area occupied by interconnects goes up faster than the area occupied by the circuits, and the crossover point at around $\lambda = 1.5$ μm or 5000 gates is soon reached where the total interconnect area is more than the device area.

2.6.3 IMPLICATIONS

(a) Local processing on the chip is cheap because it uses transistors rather than wires.
(b) Moving data between processing regions is expensive both in performance and area.

System architectures and design methodologies must take these facts into account, and likely developments are:

(1) increased attention to reducing the effects of wiring by intelligent wire management;
(2) more emphasis on system architectures which support parallel processing rather than movements of data.

2.7 Conclusions

VLSI design will always be a trade-off between conflicting requirements. On the one hand the increasing complexity of the systems being designed, the shortage of design time and the need for corrections emphasize the necessity for techniques which reduce and manage the complexity of the design. These include modularization, standardization of cells and composition methods, simple interfaces and automatic tools, all of which incur a penalty in silicon area or performance. On the other hand, the area available on the chip is always limited and pressures of cost, yield and competitive edge may force the use of techniques of optimization which inevitably blur interfaces, increase coupling between cells and hence increase complexity with attendant high risks and long design times.

At any given time there is a trade-off to be made between the highly automated, low-risk, short design time methods, and those more relevant to the use of hand crafting and highly skilled designers, but the movement towards better CAD tools and greater numbers of transistors will push the boundary between them continually upwards with time.

References

1. Steward, D.V. Analysis and complexity. In *Systems Analysis and Management*. New York: Petrocelli books (1981), p. 2.

2. Sequin, C. Managing VLSI complexity, *Proc. IEEE* **71**(1), 149–66 (1983).
3. Wirth, N. Program development by Stepwise refinement, *Commun. ACM* **14**(4), 221–7 (1971).
4. Dijkstra, E.W. The humble programmer *Commun. ACM* **15**(10), 859–66 (1972).
5. Lattin, W.W. A methodology for VLSI chip design, *Lambda*, **2**(2), 34–44 (1981).
6. Hoare, C.A.R. An axiomatic basis for computer programming, *Commun. ACM* **12**(10), 576–83 (1969).
7. Shrobe, H.E. The data path generator. In *Proc. Conf. on ADV Research in VLSI*, MIT, 175–81 (1981)

3   Layout methodologies

3.1   Introduction

There is a degree of interaction between the design tools used to produce chips and the actual implementation on silicon — sometimes known as the *architecture* or *methodology*, and also interaction between the methodology and technology. In the best systems, there is a good fit between design tools, chip architecture, and the process technology which produces efficient and elegant chip designs.

All of these — applications, CAD, methodology and technology — are a result of historical development and do not easily change; however, if a new idea appears in one area, there is often a period of time during which there is a mismatch between that area and the others while either evolutionary or revolutionary adjustments take place.

An uncommitted logic array is an example of fitting new technology and applications to an existing methodology. The methodology is that commonly taught and successfully used with SSI and MSI TTL devices, in which the primitive device is the gate, and all systems are built out of gates or combinations of gates.

It is not the only possible methodology; its success has been based on the simplifying abstraction of digital logic as opposed to analogue circuit design. Using the gate level abstraction a designer never needs to concern himself with the issues of currents and voltages; a few simple loading rules will suffice.

3.1.1   LEVELS OF ABSTRACTION

Some traditional levels of abstraction in the LSI and VLSI design hierarchy are shown on the left-hand side of Table 3.1.

These abstractions are convenient, and allow design to be carried out: for example at the circuit level (using transistors to make gates) independently of the logic level (using gates to make ALUs).

Abstractions like these have been used by a generation of discrete

Table 3.1

Processor, memory, switch	Transputer
Register transfer techniques	Data path
Gate	Structure (e.g. PLA)
Transistoer (e.g. MOSFET)	Switch networks
Material properties (e.g. silicon)	Process properties (e.g. CMOS)

component engineers and SSI engineers who developed an armoury of design methods based on their use. ULAs are chip architecture designed to make use of familiar tools and methods rather than to exploit the strengths of the silicon.

On the right-hand side of Table 3.1 are another set of abstractions which are not necessarily better or worse, but have advantages in some areas of VLSI design.

Standardization of *process properties* rather than transistor properties was done first by Mead and Conway, who derived a set of λ-based rules which could be scaled to make use of different wafer fabrication lines. Design using transistors and contacts made according to the scales as *switches* interesting and elegant *structures* can be made whose topology is clear from the network or stick diagram. This enables good layouts to be produced at a higher level than the gate level, where all knowledge of the layout topology is lost.

Concern for silicon area and performance are aspects which count for little in a ULA; it is a low risk methodology aimed at short design time at the expense of performance.

At the other extreme there are complex high-performance systems manufactured in large quantities for which area and performance are very important.

3.2 Design by abutment

Fig. 3.1 shows the c.p.u. chip for an HP9000 computer [1] in which the concern is mainly for good performance, but also for an acceptable design time and risk.

This is seen as a floor plan, consisting of relatively few high-level structures put together in a simple way. The main components in this c.p.u. chip are: a data path (registers and ALU), a decoding PLA, microprogram ROM, ROM sequencer, and a memory-processor bus (MPB).

This is an architecture used now by several successful microprocessors, the 68000 as well as the HP9000. There are several principles at the heart of the methodology used, namely:

— regularity of structure;
— orthogonality of control and data in those structures;
— connection by abutment.

The regularity and orthogonality help to make the design easy to construct and amend, and the method of abutment also minimizes the area used.

The data path in particular is constructed by running a number of 32-bit busses through it and arranging the registers and ALU components around the bus wires rather than the reverse.

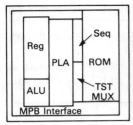

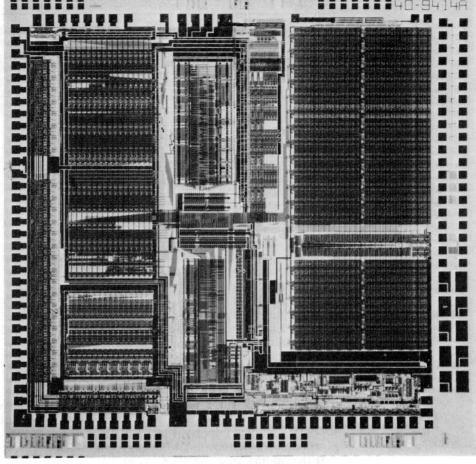

Fig. 3.1

The component cells themselves are designed as simple rectangular areas of silicon with connection points on the periphery of the rectangle.

Fig. 3.2 shows how an ALU can be fitted into a data path organization simply by abutment. Each of 32 bits of the ALU has two bus lines designed

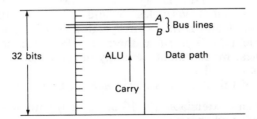

Fig. 3.2 Abutment of single bit ALU cells.

27 / Layout methodologies

into it as an integral part, as do the matching register block and shifter on either side of the ALU.

The ALU itself is often made using components which do not fit well with the gate level abstraction, i.e. a switch path.

In the switch path design of a carry circuit [2] three transistors are used to produce the output carry from the input operand bits A_n and B_n as follows

A_n	B_n	C_{out}
0	0	0
0	1	C_{in}
1	0	C_{in}
1	1	1

For all possible combinations of inputs one of the three switches in Fig. 3.3 is ON and only one, so that either circuit is connected to the positive supply, or ground, as to the carry in, depending on the values of A_n and B_n.

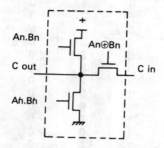

Fig. 3.3 Carry switch path.

An ALU structure based on this switch path fits particularly well with design [3] by abutment, and itself can be split down into components which support another important aspect of the design of complex systems — postponement of functional binding.

If the outline area, interconnect points, and most of the internal structure of a cell can be fixed whilst its function can still be altered, this prevents changes to the function causing knock-on effects on other cells, and considerably eases the design problems. This can be seen in the design of the ALU bit slice in Fig. 3.4.

This uses general function blocks to allow postponement of the binding and generalization of its actual function. Thus if a new ALU function is to be incorporated, it can easily be done at a late stage. The general function block itself, used for K, P, and R in Fig. 3.4, is shown in Fig. 3.5. It implements any function of two input variables A and B by decoding all the possible combinations of A and B in a switch path and using each decode to select a control variable (G_0–G_3). Since there are 16 different combination of the control variables, we can implement any of the 16 Boolean functions with the input variables (A and B).

This design of this ALU has advantages in that it is

— regular and extendable (8, 16 or 32 bits) without a change in the basic rectangular geometry;
— general (many functions);

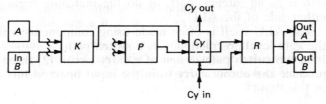

Fig. 3.4 Block diagram of one bit of the ALU.

	K	P	R	Cin	Cond	
A + B	1	6	6	0	0	Add
A + B + Cin	1	6	6	1	0	Add with carry
A − B	2	9	6	2	0	Subtract
B − A	4	9	6	2	0	Subtract reverse
A − B − Cin	2	9	6	1	0	Subtract with borrow
B − A − Cin	4	9	6	1	0	Subtract rev. w/borrow
− A	12	3	6	2	0	Negative A
− B	10	5	6	2	0	Negative B
A + 1	3	12	6	2	0	Increment A
B + 1	5	10	6	2	0	Increment B
A − 1	12	3	9	2	0	Decrement A
B − 1	10	5	9	2	0	Decrement B
A∧B	0	8	12	0	0	Logical And
A∨B	0	14	12	0	0	Logical Or
A⊕B	0	6	12	0	0	Logical Exor
¬A	0	3	12	0	0	Not A
¬B	0	5	12	0	0	Not B
A	0	12	12	0	0	A
B	0	10	12	0	0	B
Mul	1	14	14	0	1	Multiply step
Div	3	15	15	0	2	Divide step
A/O	0	14	12	0	3	Conditional And/Or
Mask	10	5	8	2	0	Generate mask

Any of 16 functions of 2 variables

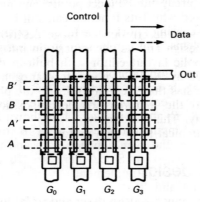

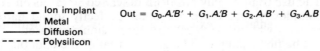

Out = $G_0.A'.B' + G_1.A'.B + G_2.A.B' + G_3.A.B$

- - - Ion implant
——— Metal
——— Diffusion
----- Polysilicon

Fig. 3.5

29 / Layout methodologies

— rectangular in shape (will fit into the data path easily);
— economical in area (10–20% of a gate level design).

However, it is relatively slow. In a carry lookahead adder it is possible to have a regular design, which is also fast. Fig. 3.6 gives the general schematic of a 16-bit lookahead adder with two levels of lookahead, each over four stages, in this design:

— regularity exists;
— higher-level lookahead blocks have exactly the same design as low-level blocks but need to be stretched to fit a rectangular overall floor plan;
— width is predictable, but height less easily so;
— it is not easy to fit within a data path because alterations in numbered bits also alter the height, affecting the floor plan of the data path.

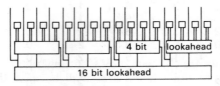

Fig. 3.6 Carry lookahead.

3.2.1 SPECIAL PURPOSE DESIGN TOOLS

Low risk design styles are often supported by a comprehensive CAD system in which the physical details or even the overall floor plan are not under the control of the user. Styles of design in which there is a premium on silicon area usually require a graphical input and involve an element of risk as to whether the actual layout corresponds to the original intent of the designer. There are now tools which support the design style of the previous section, yet maintain correctness by constraining the layout to conform to a structure defined by a high-level language, notably from INMOS. [4] This system includes

(1) A hardware description language describing the structure and function of the design and its decomposition into sub-units.
(2) A symbolic layout editor with built-in design rules. The connectivity described by the HDL is enforced at each level in the hierarchy, but the designer has the freedom to divide the physical chip area as he wishes, provided the hierarchy of decomposition always matches the HDL hierarchy. This is done by
(3) A hierarchical floor plan editor.

3.3 Hierarchy in hardware design

The use of hierarchy has been described so far as an aid to the management of complexity, but there are other perfectly sound hardware cost–performance reasons why hierarchical structures should be used.

The first example to be given is that of the data bus in a processor. A typical scheme is shown in Fig. 3.7 in which a simple two-phase clock system is used to transfer information between three units. Because the layout and method of interconnection of each unit of the bus is simple, it is possible to join as many units on the end as desired without altering the overall scheme.

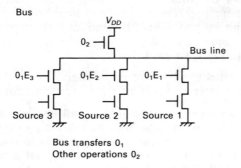

Fig. 3.7

The physical units are connected by 'abutting' one to the next and the silicon area requirements of the scheme are small because the interconnections are reduced to zero length. This works well if the busses are relatively short, but the speed is a function of the number of units connected to the bus.

Bus capacitance increases for each new unit, slowing the operation of the whole bus for each clock phase. This can be overcome by making the transistor sizes a function of the number of units, but the larger drive transistors need to be driven themselves and therefore may affect the internal cell design. Also these transistors are part of a cell themselves, so that one cell is affected by others external to itself — a recipe for a complex design.

Better is to design each unit with a standard interface capable of driving four

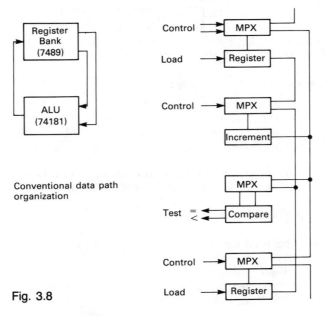

Fig. 3.8

or five others local to it, with a higher level joining four or five groups of units. This kind of scheme has been used in the data path design method of one 'silicon compiler'.

Fig. 3.8 shows the MacPitts data path as compared with a conventional arrangement where registers are grouped together, and data is always sent to an arithmetic unit for processing. Instead local short paths can be provided for frequently used routes, as well as the slow global data path. Local paths can be fast, and the hardware so used that:

(a) Several paths can operate in parallel.
(b) Units that interact frequently are provided with a dedicated path.

The overall hardware now goes faster, and the design no longer interacts in a complex way since we accept that the infinitely extensible global data path will be slow, and do not increase transistor sizes to complete.

Only the local communications here are fast, but it may also be possible to make the global path fast in a hierarchical system. In order to understand how this seemingly impossible feat can be achieved it is necessary to look at a closely related problem where it is possible to make sufficient simplification to produce a general result. Fig. 3.9 shows the fan-out tree problem.

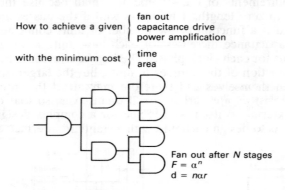

How to achieve a given $\left\{ \begin{array}{l} \text{fan out} \\ \text{capacitance drive} \\ \text{power amplification} \end{array} \right.$

with the minimum cost $\left\{ \begin{array}{l} \text{time} \\ \text{area} \end{array} \right.$

Fan out after N stages
$F = \alpha^n$
$d = n\alpha r$

Min delay when $\alpha = e$, min area when $\alpha = F$

Fi.g 3.9 Fan out tree problem.

3.3.1 THE FAN-OUT TREE PROBLEM

Here the branching ratio, α, at each stage in a fan-out tree can be optimized. The number of levels, n, is related to α and F by

$$\log_e F = n \log_e \alpha$$

Thus the total delay is

$$d = \frac{\log_e F}{\log_e \alpha} \alpha \tau$$

which has a minimum when $\alpha = 2.718$. It therefore pays to have a hierarchy in terms of speed but not in terms of area.

3.4 RAM system

The advantages of hierarchy in simplifying the design problem are very real and can be illustrated by the dynamic RAM chip. The aim in a RAM chip is to get as many bits per chip as possible with a given yield, but a secondary aim is to get a good performance.

Figure 3.10 shows the circuit and some possible layouts of an NMOS dynamic RAM cell. The normal cell is made as small as possible and consists of a select transistor and capacitor. The basic limitation to reduction in size is the ratio of storage capacitance C_s to total capacitance on the bit line $C_S + C_B$ which reduces the voltage available to the sense amplifier. If the size is too small, then the output voltage on the bit line, which is proportional to $V_{dd}C_s/(C_S + C_B)$ will be too low to give an adequate signal to the noise ratios.

Arrays of these cells are arranged in blocks within a RAM chip and a typical 16K RAM chip is organized in two blocks of 8K [5], as shown in Fig. 3.11.

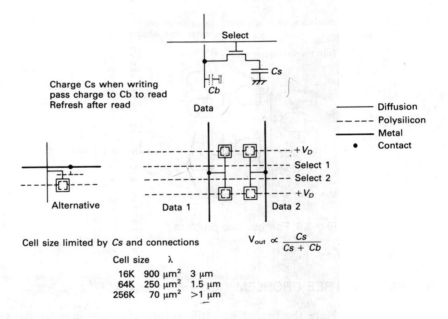

Fig. 3.10

Because of the small output voltage available, the system must be sensed differentially by a regenerative sense amplifier, which also refreshes the storage node. A schematic of the organization of the chip in Fig. 3.11 is shown in Fig. 3.12.

It is characteristic of this type of sense circuit that the time delay required to give a valid output from a small sense voltage is given by

Fig. 3.11

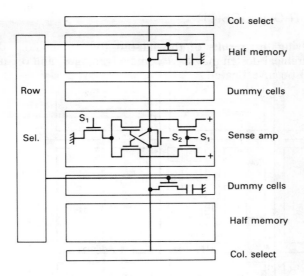

Fig. 3.12 Organization.

$$CR \log_e \frac{V_{H-L}}{V_{A-B}}$$

where V_{H-L} is the difference between a stored '1' and a stored '0' and V_{A-B} is the difference between the bit lines after the charge from the memory cell has been distributed in the bit-line capacitance.

C is the bit-line capacitance, and in a square array is proportional to $(bits)^{\frac{1}{2}}$. The voltage V_{A-B} is approximately proportional to $(bits)^{-\frac{1}{2}}$, since it is itself proportional to C^{-1}.

Because the sense delay is proportional to C, it will increase at a rate greater than $(bits)^{\frac{1}{2}}$ as the chip size is increased. There is also a delay in selecting a row of memory cells because the select lines are usually polysilicon and have a delay proportional to $(length)^2$. As the chip increases in size, therefore, the sense delay times increase at a rate proportional to $(bits)^{\frac{1}{2}}$, and the access delay times at a rate proportional to the number of bits.

The total delay in the system lies somewhere between $\alpha(bits)^{\frac{1}{2}}$ and $\alpha(bits)$, usually closer to a direct proportionality to the number of bits. It is only because the feature size reduces on the chip between successive generations of RAM chips that the total access time does not actually increase. This style of design (but abutment of cells) has led to a very large number of bits packed on the chip, but the speed does not improve with scaling as one would expect, and other design problems include

(1) ever-increasing voltage margins for the sense amplifier;
(2) a difficult design problem since many factors interact (bit cell, sense amplifier, noise margins, select drivers).

3.5 Hierarchical memory design

Applying the results of the fan-out tree to memory design suggests that a hierarchical design may have some advantages, and organizations like Fig. 3.13 could be investigated.

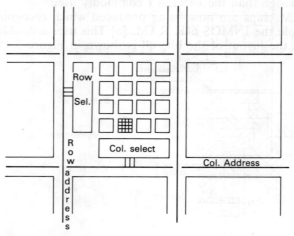

Fig. 3.13 Hierarchical organization.

The optimum branching ratio in this organization depends on a number of factors:

— the overheads in area needed for decoding and sensing;
— the area–time trade off required;
— the system characteristics (which lines are polysilicon, the performance of the sense amplifier).

Typically there is an optimum, and if the hierarchy can be arranged to

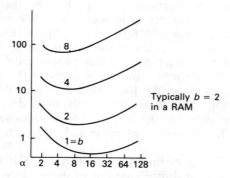

Fig. 3.14

prevent the design of lower levels from affecting higher levels, the complexity and design problem is eased.

Fig. 3.14 shows a family of curves with the cost criterion of area × time plotted against branching ratio for various ratios of RAM cell area. It clearly shows that branching ratios between 4×4:1 and 32×32:1 should give a lower cost design than the 64×128:1 commonly used.

RAM chips are now being produced which recognize these principles, for example the INMOS 64K RAM. [6] This uses a double polysilicon process in which the layout of the bit cell is shown in Figure 3.15.

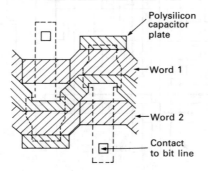

Fig. 3.15 64K RAM bit cell.

Here the capacitance of the cell is only 0.050 pF and there are severe problems in detecting a small sense voltage in the face of a large variation in processing parameters and significant noise. The solution is to divide and conquer. The 64K bits are organized on the chip as eight blocks of 8K rather than two of 32K, as shown in Fig. 3.16. This is on the principle that it is more difficult to design a 64K memory in the same way as a 16K memory than it is to simply shrink four 16K memories and put them together on the chip.

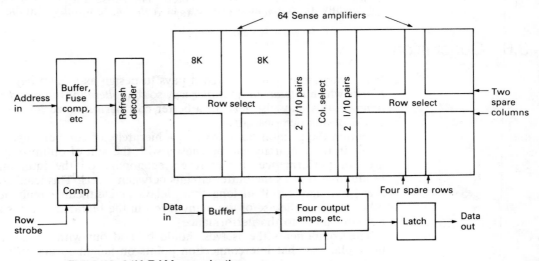

Fig. 3.16 64K RAM organization.

37 / Layout methodologies

In the actual circuitry some other interesting methods are used to share the sense amplifiers between four bit lines rather than two, which are indicated in Fig. 3.17.

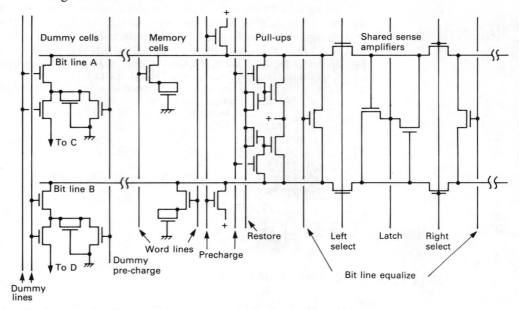

Fig. 3.17 Circuit design.

Here dummy cells are changed to the full supply voltage rather than $\frac{1}{2}V_{dd}$, and the mechanism for provided a half charge for comparison with the stored memory cell charge is to distribute the full charge on two lines A and C when a memory cell on bit line B is selected. The sense amplifiers is switched to the left-hand side and senses the voltage differences between A and B.

3.6   Conclusions

It is always true that in design it pays to design as a *hierarchy of well-defined blocks* which *interact in a simpler way* so that *alterations in one do not affect the other* — this may also lead to a better cost performance for the hardware, as RAM design demonstrates.

Within the general framework of a hierarchy of components, the number of levels in the hierarchy can be chosen with the aim of optimizing either silicon area or performance. Fewer levels economize on the interconnection area required as well as the buffer circuits between levels. This leads to small silicon area, but may result in long time delays and difficult circuit design. At the other extreme the use of too many levels in the hierarchy wastes area and may not contribute to the performance.

The components themselves should be laid out with a view to the overall floor plan, so that interconnection points on neighbouring cells are adjacent, and control and data lines are orthogonal. This leads to good wire management, and coupled with a top-down approach in which the floor planning phase is followed by detailed design of the sub-cells makes for an elegant final layout with little space wasted on interconnect area.

References

1. Beyers, J. *et al.* A32b VLSI chip. *Digest of Technical Papers*, IEFE International Solid State Circuits Conference, THAM 9.1 (1981).
2. Kilburn, T. *et al.* A parallel arithmetic unit wring a saturated transistor fast carry unit. *PROC IEE*, **107B**, 573–84 (1960).
3. Mead, C. and Conway, L. *Introduction to VLSI Systems*. Addison-Wesley (1980).
4. Chesney, M. INMOS design approach and associated tools. In *VLSI Architecture* edited by Randell, B. and Trealeven, P. Prentice-Hall (1983).
5. Ahlquist, C.N. *et al.* A 16384-bit dynamic RAM, *IEEE J. Solid State Circuits*, **SCii**(5), 570–3 (1976).
6. Eaton, S.S. *et al.* Circuit advances propel 64K RAM across the 100 nS barrier. *Electronics*, **55**(6), 132–6 (1982).

4 Design systems

4.1 Introduction

Integrated circuit or digital hardware design systems generally have the aim of providing a comprehensive set of tools to verify and lay out the design, and to assist in the testing of production circuits. One great advantage of a properly integrated design system is that a single circuit description is used throughout this process, ensuring that the same circuit is laid out on the chip as was originaly simulated. If the simulator requires a separate input from the auto layout, with a hand translation process in between, the chances of error are very great.

The steps involved in the design of a gate array using a fairly simple design system incorporating simulation, testability analysis and autorouting, but relying on hand placement, are shown in Fig. 4.1. This format is fairly representative of a number of gate array systems, although the location of the software may vary: for example, simulation and testability analysis may be done on the designer's site, whereas the auto route software may reside with the semiconductor manufacturer because it is more specific to the actual architecture.

4.1.1 INPUT

Most designers are familiar with digital design using gates and logic diagrams. This is a convenient abstraction well supported by a body of existing knowledge, and may be used if is possible to enter the circuit description on a graphics screen using logic symbols interconnected by lines to represent the structure of the circuit.

A simpler form of input, however, is to use a text file in which hardware blocks and interconnections are given names. Thus a gate is described by a gate type, output signals, input signals end of gate marker, and optionally other things may be added, e.g. gate position on the array where control is required of placement, position on a diagram, or a unique identifier for each gate

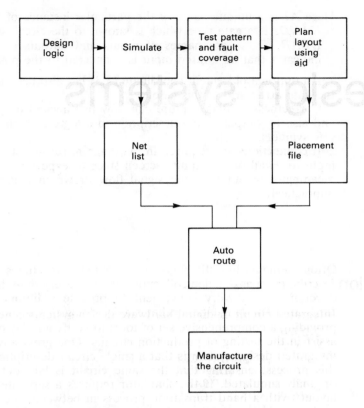

Fig. 4.1 Design process.

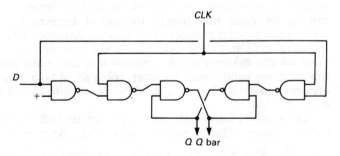

Fig. 4.2 Circuit fragment.

instance. The position of the signal name in the line implies which input or output is connected to that string of connected points. A typical input fragment [1] is given below, and describes the logic diagram of Fig. 4.2.

In this description each component gate or subcircuit is on a single line such as

A1: (3,3) *NAND2* [*DBAR, D, +*]

Here *A1* is a unique name of the particular instance of *NAND2*

NAND2 is a gate type which is known to the circuit compiler

DBAR, D . . . are names of inputs and outputs to the NAND gate (+ indicates that an unused input is connected to the positive supply)

An optional placement coordinate (3,3) has also been added to locate *A1* on the gate array grid in this case.

Correctness of data capture can now be checked by parsing the input file, and also by output of the description in a logic diagram form with AND and OR symbols.

If connections are required in the diagram (drawn strings) these are usually input in detail on a graphics screen since to expect the software to provide a meaningful layout with the signal flow drawn in a logical way is presently impractical.

4.1.2 MACROS

Often elements like flip flops are repeated many times. It is not sensible to describe them as detailed collections of gates every time that particular element is required, and very convenient to provide a library of useful blocks of hardware. The language mechanism for doing this is the subcircuit or macro.

```
DEFINE
SUBCIR
  DLAT [Q,QBAR:D,CLK]
  A1: NAND 2 [DBAR,D,+]
  A2: NAND2 [R,DBAR,CLK]
  A3: NAND2 [S,D,CLK]
  A4: NAND2[QBAR,Q,R,]
  A5: NAND2[Q,QBAR,S]
ENDM
```

The compiler can now replace the call of a macro:

S2: DLAT[Q5,I5,STRB]

By its equivalent series of gates with the formal signal names, *Q, D, CLK*, replaced by actual signal names, *O5, I5, STRB*, and internal signals and instances modified by concatenating the unique macro instance name *S2* with each of them.

A hierarchy of user-defined macros can be built up in thus way with macros calling macros. This hierarchy has several advantages:

— It reduces the amount of text required to specify a design.
— It makes the design easier to understand.
— It contains extra information (as compared with a purely gate level description) on which gates should be grouped together which can be used by the system to help layout, and simulation.

If the design is to be in logic diagram form, there are different styles of diagram which can be used. Two of these are shown in Fig. 4.3.

Gate symbols are appropriate if a relatively small section of the diagram is to be shown, and the connections between gates, if drawn, can help understading of the network.

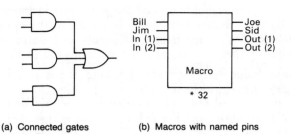

(a) Connected gates   (b) Macros with named pins

Fig. 4.3

It is obvious that for very complex systems, described at the high level, a diagram is less useful than text because drawn connections are difficult to follow, and the different kinds of macros are not easily distinguishable from each other by eye because they are all drawn as square boxes. At this level text is needed on the diagram to identify the signal names, paths and macro names, and the great advantage of instant recognition of the signal flow in a diagram no longer applies.

The next step in the design process is to analyse the input text and create an internal representation of the network. This internal representation may either flatten the hierarchy to gate level or retain it.

The first option is the easiest to implement, but the resulting data structure will be large since every gate now has to be individually stored. Computation time for the rest of the CAD tools will also be long because each gate is treated individually.

The second is better — macros can be laid out *once* and simply copied where needed. This exploits the hierarchy for layout, since it is likely that the components of a macro need to be close to each other. Simulators may also be able to take advantage of the hierarchy since the network may be simulated in terms of gates (primitives) or macros. If the simulator has a high-level behavioural description of the macro which does not need to be subdivided into gates, a faster simulation will result.

4.2 Libraries

Each of the primitive gates described in the input text usually has a corresponding model built in the simulator and enable the overall circuit to be checked, and the layout system needs to have information on the area occupied by a gate and the input–output pin positions before detailed layout can be done.

In the case of a ULA, many of these primitives are simple gates that occupy either one or a few cells on the chip. The complete chip may consist of an array of 2400 cells laid out in rows as shown in Fig. 4.4, each row of 160 cells being spaced from its neighbour by a wiring channel intended for the interconnections. A single cell is made up of four or five transistors laid out so that a range of gates can be constructed simply by using one or two layers of interconnecting metal. A CMOS layout for a cell is given in Fig. 4.5 and two possible gate variations based on the cell are illustrated in Fig. 4.6.

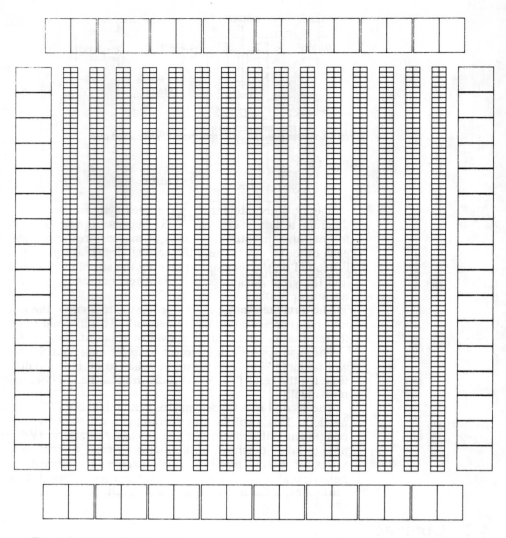

Fig. 4.4 2400 cell gate array.

A designer's productivity is much greater if he or she operates at a high level, using proven macros consisting of groups of cells rather than reinventing subcircuits from primitives in each design. This pressure encourages the growth of design libraries of relatively complex cells as well as a library of primitives.

A great deal of information is required by the layout, simulation, and text generation software which must be in the various libraries. Each primitive and subcircuit may have some or all of the following information stored:

(1)   the detailed layout and pin positions;
(2)   the formal parameter names;
(3)   how to draw it on a logical diagram;
(4)   a behavioural description for use in the simulator;

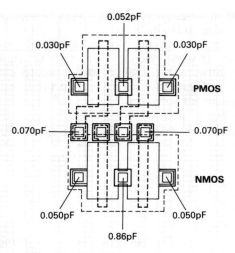

TRACK CAPACITANCE:
Layer One 0.29pF/100mil
Layer Two 0.21pF/100mil

Fig. 4.5 Array element.

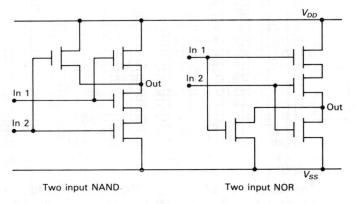

Two input NAND.   Two input NOR

Fig. 4.6

(5) a statement of whether it is made up of other subcircuits, and if so where to find these in the library;

(6) information on the electrical design rules associated with each pin, to ensure it is used correctly.

If all the different versions of all the different kinds of elements are needed, the library can soon get very large. For example there may be 10 ways of laying out a NOR gate (inputs and outputs in different places), 5 different sorts of flip flop (each could be made from any combination of differeent gates), 2 bit registers, 4-bit, 8-bit ALUs, adders, multipliers, etc. It is clearly impossible to put in a library all possible elements that could be made, and we must be content with a few representative examples. The problem of keeping the library up to date in a design system is a very serious one, since users always want the latest device to be included.

It is important here to keep the physical details of a macro together with the behavioural details. In some systems the two are separate, the behaviour being embedded in the software of the simulator, or incorporated in the input text of the simulator run and therefore separate from the layout information which is held with the auto layout software. The advantage of holding both in a library is that it is possible to prevent one being changed without the other being updated. Leaving the two separate means that inevitably, with a large number of elements being entered and altered, they will get out of step, so that the actual layout will not correspond with the simulated network.

4.3 Parameterization

One way of reducing the explosion of data is to introduce parameterization into the *subcircuit description*, and make it more like a procedure in a high-level language. The beginnings of parameterization are shown in the following description, where the signal Y is defined as an array (0 to 3).

```
! A two-input four-output decoder !
    SUBCIR/UCATAL
        DECODE [Y<0:3>:EN,A,B]
        DECLARE/DQ<0:3>
        D1:   NAND2 [ABAR,A +]
        D2:   NAND2 [BBAR,B, +]
        D3:   NAND2[DQ <0>, ABAR, BBAR]
        D4:   NAND2 [DQ <1>, ABAR, B]
        D5:   NAND2 [DQ <2>, A,      BBAR]
        D6:   NAND2 [DQ <3>, A,      B]
        D7:   NAND2 [Y    <0>, DQ <0>, EN]
        D8:   NAND2 [Y    <1>, DQ <1>, EN]
        D9:   NAND2 [Y    <2>, DQ >2>, EN]
        D10: NAND2 [Y    <3>, DQ <3>, EN]
    ENDM
```

*The User CATA*Logue modifier after the keyword *SUBCIR* tells the compiler to save this description in the user library for subsequent use without the need to keep defining the decoder in every new gate array description. The declaration of an intermediate signal $DQ <0:3>$ is needed here as there is no other place where the dimensions (0 to 3) of this signal are explicitly given. The shorthand of grouping 4- or 32-bit busses under a signal name can save a great deal of tedious writing. For example,

```
A1: REG [Q OUT <0:32>, DIN <0:32>, CLOCK]
```

Clearly much more could be done to improve the readability of the input as well as to reduce the number of different subcircuits stored in the library. A few systems parameterize the subcircuit description to a much greater extent producing generic part types rather than the single part descriptions above. [2] This technique allows a p-input, 2^p-output decoder to be designed, but requires the notion of integer variables for loops and parameters other than signals to be included in the description language. In this case the decoder call might be

$A1$: $DECODE$ (3) [OUT <1:8>, EN, $ADDR$ <1:3>]

with the parameter of size included in the round brackets. Since most, if not all, the constructs needed are present in existing high-level programming languages, it is natural to think of using existing languages to describe hardware, and subsequent chapters show how this can be done.

4.4 Design management

The problem of the library becomes greater if we consider a large design with many engineers working on it, using a library which is being constantly updated.

Suppose the design required is an advanced processor in which designer A produces the address calculation arithmetic using a library ALU, and proves it correct by simulating. Later a new design of ALU with the same function but which operates at a faster speed is produced.

Designer B designs a floating point unit using the new ALU, and proves his unit correct. Will the part made by A work with the new ALU? Will A's address modifier work with the new part? And when we recompile the chip which version should we use?

Questions like these need to be answered if libraries of compoents are going to be used on a large scale, and insertion and deletion of library information needs to be rigidly controlled, but unfortunately 'everybody wants to put something in, but no-one wants to take anything out.' [3]

4.4.1 FILE SYSTEMS

The simplest method of controlling a library is to maintain a collection of files, which can be protected by the operating system of the computer on which they reside from unauthorized additions and deletions. Typically three types of files may exist.

(1) *Basic technology libraries*, which contain a set of primitives appropriate to a particular technology, e.g. CMOS, NMOS or BIPOLAR. These are supplied and characterized by the manufacturer of the gate array and may not be altered in any way by users.

(2) *Subcircuit libraries*. These are produced by teams of designers wishing to use devices at a higher level than the basic primitives, and defining subcircuit models which allow simulation at a higher level than decomposition into primitives would allow. All members of the design team can be allowed access to the library to incorporate the subcircuits in their section of the system, but only a few may be authorized to add new, proved subcircuits to the library.

(3) *User libraries*. A user may wish to create a range of subcircuits for his own particular application, but may have deliberately designed one to economize on silicon area, knowing that it will only be used in a certain way.

Whilst useful to someone who is aware of its restrictions, it would not be made available for general use and should be kept in a private user library not accessible to others.

4.4.2 DEPENDENCIES

In a very large design, work will proceed in parallel on different parts of the chip or system, with a team of designers creating many libraries of circuits. One part of the chip may rely on the use of a separate subcircuit or module which subsequently undergoes a change, and it is useful to be able to indicate when the date of creation of a subcircuit is later than the data in the design file which uses it. One solution to this problem is to describe the dependency relations and the creation dates of the current modules, taking the required action to keep the parts of the system consistent. [4]

4.4.3 DATA BASES

In the long term, library systems based on files, however sophisticated the protection and management tools, will eventually evolve into data bases because of the need to interface a range of design programs to the same library information and to query the library during the design process.

Future library components will have a behavioural specification held in the data base as well as the circuit structure intended to fulfil this specification. The two can then be checked against each other for consistency — has the designer properly fulfilled the original intent? This means that as well as simulators requiring the specification from the database, tools for demonstrating the equivalence will also require access to the specification data.

The growth of paramaterized libraries of generic cells opens the possibility of cells parameterized for area–performance trade-offs as well as the simple size parameters described earlier. A designer might then reasonably expect to query the data base for the range of cells available to fulfill a particular application.

4.5 Circuit and function extraction

Ideally a design system captures the input at the gate or higher level, and provided this description is correct, the chip is automatically compiled to conform to this description.

In the quest for speed improvement or area minimization, it is sometimes felt necessary to check the final layout for capacitive loading effects, which may produce a slightly different performance from that simulated before the layout was known, or to put in tracks by hand where auto layout techniques are unable to find paths.

Programs exist to reconstruct the circuit to ensure correctness or to measure the actual performance. The technique involves the identification of the design from the mask level to either transistor or gate level. The networks can then be resimulated at gate or circuit level.

Usually the transistors in a gate array cell are linked together by a number of distinct metal link patterns to form different kinds of gates. These gates are then connected by tracks on the available connection mask layer(s) to customize the array to the required network. Fig. 4.7 shows how the separate links and tracks can be recombined to reconstruct the network from a layout file consisting of links and tracks.

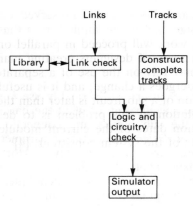

Fig. 4.7 Verification structure.

Function or circuit extraction is a common technique which has some advantages and disadvantages.

Good points

— The design can be changed at the low level, e.g. replacing an OR gate with a wired OR to save space. Resimulating ensures correctness.
— Electrical rules can be checked, and detailed timing simulation can be done with the actual connection paths extracted from the masks.

Bad points

— This kind of program operates at a very low level, and may have to examine millions of mask shapes in a large chip — a very time-consuming process.
— Signal names are lost at the mask level. This makes it difficult to resimulate (internal names can be different).
— Structure is lost, including useful information such as which flip flops belong to which registers.
— It is not easy to identify all possible layouts of a macro from the masks; only those layouts stored in the library can be recognized by a matching process.

4.5.1 INCLUDING PRAGMATS IN THE INPUT DESCRIPTION

One method of achieving control over layout avoids the problems of reconstruction after intervention and the difficulties of graphics by going back to the input.

If the input contains a way to specify the placement, or to fix the wire routing in parts of the design, other parts can be left for layout programs to complete. The fixed information can be altered (the pragmats) and the design recompiled, perhaps deleting some fixed wiring between macros and altering the placement of others until a good result is achieved. Here the layout will always be correct since it is automatically done, and the job of interaction is done at a higher and more convenient level for the designer. The way in which the intervention was carried out is also preserved on file in the input text pragmats so that a design can be recompiled from that text alone.

4.6   Future trends

The design systems of the future will probably use *high-level* input language, which includes both the specification of what the hardware is supposed to do and the structure of the sub blocks and connections, i.e. how to do it. Components will exist *in design data bases* as parameterized procedures with parameters to indicate size, and possibly performance–area trade-offs. Management of the data involved in the libraries and partially completed designs will require sophisticated data base techniques.

The user will write a program to describe his hardware making full use of general software constructs and methods to make the design flexible and readable. Auto layout methods will then compile the chip making use of any pragmats provided by the designer to guide the layout, and verification tools will be used to check the correctness of the design.

References

1. Plessey. *The CLASSIC Manual*, Plessey Semiconductors, Swindon (1984).
2. Gray, J.P. Designing gate arrays using a silicon compiler, *Proc 19th Design Automation Conference* (Las Vegas) (1982).
3. Wienber, G.M. *The Psychology of Computer Programming*, Van Nostrand Reinhold, New York (1971).
4. Feldman, S.I. Make — a program for maintaining computer programs. *Software — practice and experience*, **9** 255–65 (1979).

5 PLA based design

5.1 Introduction

The Programmable Logic Array, or PLA as it is usually known, is a method for implementing logic functions on silicon using a regular structure. In terms of design effort and cost, it lies somewhere between the gate array and full custom design using random logic. Like the gate array, the PLA reduces design and verification time by using a regular array of cells which are guaranteed to be correct — the method of customization for a particular function is the addition of some simple, easily checked elements to the fixed part of the architecture. Unlike the gate array, however, the PLA is of variable size and uses a standard full-custom fabrication process with all the associated mask steps. This increases production costs, but provides a more flexible approach since other design styles may be mixed on the same chip. Gate arrays are necessarily limited in this respect, since the array designer cannot anticipate all possible uses of the chip and must make compromises.

A major advantage of the PLA is that it exploits the fact that wires become more expensive than transistors in terms of speed and area on the scale encountered in VLSI. Since the wiring pattern in a PLA is pre-ordained in the form of a regular, compact grid, it does not suffer from the routing channel difficulties to which gate arrays are prone.

5.2 Structural principles of the PLA

5.2.1 THEORETICAL BASIS FOR THE PLA

It is common knowledge that any Boolean function can be represented in canonical form as a sum of minterms or a product of maxterms. [1] We shall choose the former for illustration here. For example, the sum output for a full adder can be written as

$$S = A \oplus B \oplus C$$

51 / PLA based design

which can be rewritten as

$$S = A.\bar{B}.\bar{C} + \bar{A}.B.\bar{C} + \bar{A}.\bar{B}.C + A.B.C$$

There are four separate product terms in this example.

Most logic circuits have more than one output, each being drived from a set of common inputs by a separate function. In many cases, some common product terms arise and these need only be implemented once no matter how many functions contain them. For example, consider these arbitrary functions of four inputs:

$$Z_0 = \bar{X}_0 \, X_1 \, X_2 \, X_3$$
$$Z_1 = X_0 \, \bar{X}_1 \, X_2 \, \bar{X}_3 + \bar{X}_0 \, X_1 \, X_2 \, X_3 + X_1 \, \bar{X}_3$$
$$Z_2 = X_1 \, \bar{X}_3 + \bar{X}_0 \, \bar{X}_1 \, \bar{X}_3$$
$$Z_3 = \bar{X}_0 \, X_1 \, X_2 \, X_3 + X_1 \, \bar{X}_3 + X_0 \, \bar{X}_1 \, X_2 \, \bar{X}_3$$

Here, there are nine product terms, only five of which are distinct.

5.2.2 COMPONENTS OF THE PLA

There are three basic operations to be performed when implementing a function in this form; generation of complements of the inputs, formation of the individual product terms, then summation of the terms to give the outputs. The PLA is a generalized implementation of the operations in which all the inputs and their complements are available to a series of AND gates (one per product term) and all the product terms produced are available to a series of OR gates (one per output) as shown in Fig. 5.1. The specific function required is 'programmed' by connecting the required inputs to the gates.

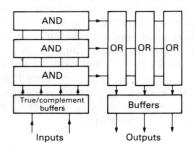

Fig. 5.1 Block diagram of a PLA.

5.2.3 TOPOLOGY OF THE PLA

It is customary to construct the gates as long, thin structures which have their inputs along the long side and the output on the short side. This allows them to be stacked as in Fig. 5.1 to create the AND plane and OR plane, the OR plane being orthogonal to the AND plane. The input true/complement buffers and output buffers can be stacked along the bottom edge.

An interesting property of this structure is that rows or columns can be swapped without changing the basic structure. Another possibility is that the output buffers can be placed along the top. This allows routing of connections to other parts of the chip to be simplified by choosing the PLA input and output positions in a suitable manner.

5.3 NMOS technology

5.3.1 NMOS PLA CIRCUIT

The basic gate types in NMOS technology are NAND and NOR. The AND and OR planes could be constructed from either or a combination of these, but in practice NOR gates are used in preference for both planes. This is because the NAND gate requires a series connection of transistors which means that the widths of the transistors must be increased so that the output logic levels may be maintained. NOR gates with their parallel structure do not need this, hence their use in the PLA. A circuit diagram of such a PLA is shown in Fig. 5.2 and the corresponding layout is shown in Fig. 5.3.

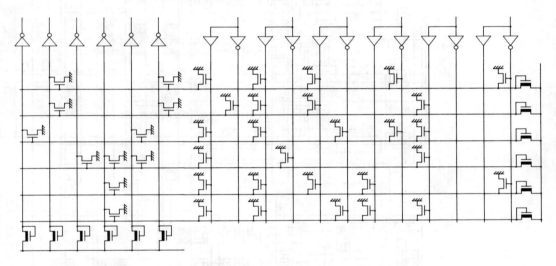

Fig. 5.2 Circuit of an NMOS PLA.

The AND plane gates are formed as rows with a depletion mode pull-up transistor at the left and the output at the right on the metal layer. The inputs run vertically on polysilicon and form the gates of the pull-down transistors. Ground connections for the pull-downs run vertically on diffusion. The OR plane structure is identical except for a 90° rotation.

The positions of the programming transistors in Fig. 5.3 are emphasized by shading. A rectangle of diffusion and a metal-diffusion contact are used for each pull-down; adjacent columns share contacts. The input and output buffers are made using NMOS inverters with high current drive capability.

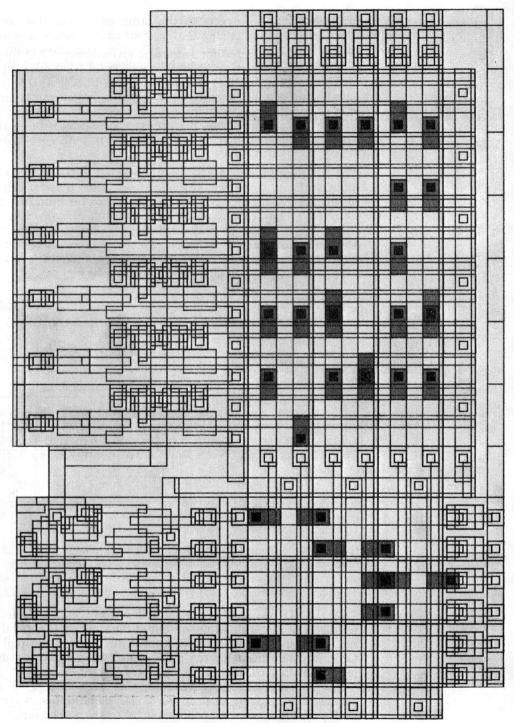

Fig. 5.3 Layout of an NMOS PLA.

The PLA is well suited for automatic layout using CAD tools and a program called PLAGEN is in use at the University of Newcastle for this purpose. [2] The information necessary to characterize a PLA is its size (number of inputs, outputs and product terms) and its function, which can be expressed as tables of ones and zeros or 'bit maps' for the AND and OR planes. The presence of a one in the table indicates the presence of a transistor in the corresponding place in the layout. The data for the PLA in Fig. 5.3 is shown in Table 5.1.

Table 5.1

```
00                    (layout origin x,y)
      6   6   3       (inputs, outputs, feedbacks)
      6               (product terms)
1 0 0 0 1 0 0 1 0 1 0 1   (AND plane)
0 0 0 1 0 0 0 1 0 1 1 0
0 0 0 1 1 0 1 0 0 1 0 1
0 0 0 1 0 0 0 0 1 0 0 1
1 0 0 0 0 1 0 1 0 1 0 1
0 0 0 1 0 1 1 0 0 1 0 1

      1 0 0 0 1 0       (OR plane)
      1 0 0 0 1 0
      0 1 0 0 0 1
      0 1 1 1 0 0
      0 0 1 0 0 0
```

The program lays out the PLA as a set of standard parts and then overlays this with the programming transistor parts. The final result is a description in the GAELIC language of the mask patterns required. The PLA parts used are from a library of NMOS structures developed at Xerox PARC in the USA. [3]

5.4 CMOS technology

5.4.1 THE STATIC CMOS PLA

It is possible to design a CMOS PLA in the same way as an NMOS PLA by building large NAND or NOR gates. Unfortunately, both types of gate incorporate both a series and a parallel structure. As can be seen in Fig. 5.4 the basic cell requires two transistors instead of one. Where a gate input is needed, a p-channel device is inserted in the series pull-up chain and an n-channel device in the parallel pull-down chain. This doubles the size of the plane compared to the NMOS design.

5.4.2 THE DYNAMIC CMOS PLA

It is possible to reduce the area of the CMOS PLA by making use of a clock to pre-charge the gate outputs so that only half the transistors are needed. [4] In the PLA section shown in Fig. 5.5, when the clock ϕ is low, the output is pulled

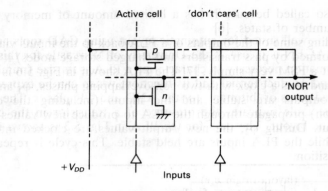

Fig. 5.4 Section of a static CMOS PLA.

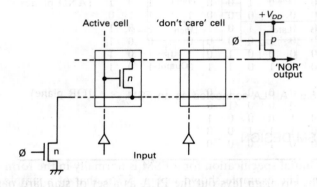

Fig. 5.5 Section of a clocked CMOS PLA.

high and the pull-downs disabled. When φ goes high, the pull-downs are enabled and the pull-up disabled, allowing the capacitive output lines to be selectively discharged. The output will remain valid only until leakage causes the charge to decay.

Various schemes are available to implement dynamic CMOS PLAs, involving various types of clocking and buffering at the inputs and outputs and between planes. [5]

5.5 PLAs as finite state machines

5.5.1 THE FINITE STATE MACHINE

Many digital systems must perform some sort of sequential operation. Sometimes this may be explicit — for example in a traffic light controller — sometimes it may be purely for convenience in implementation — for example in a serial multiplier. Sequential circuits must contain both a memory for past input values and some combinational logic to compute the response to past and present inputs. An abstract model for this is the finite state machine (FSM) which is so called because it has a limited amount of memory and hence a limited number of states. [6]

By feeding some of the outputs of a PLA back to the inputs via storage cells (usually formed by pass transistors and charged storage nodes) it is possible to implement a FSM very simply. [7] The PLA shown in Fig. 5.6 is connected in this way and uses a clock with two non-overlapping phases, ϕ_1 and ϕ_2. During ϕ_1, the outputs are stable and the inputs (including the current state information) propagate through the PLA to produce new values for the state and output. During ϕ_2, the new output values are clocked into the output latches while the PLA inputs are held stable. This cycle is repeated for each state transition.

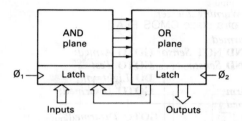

Fig. 5.6 A PLA connected as an FSM.

5.5.2 CAD TOOLS FOR FSM DESIGN

The initial specification for a FSM is normally in the form of a state diagram or table. The example shown in Fig. 5.7 is that of a simple burglar alarm.

Inputs: A = Arm
        D = Disarm
        S = Sensor

Outputs: B = Bell
         L = Light
         W = Warning buzzer

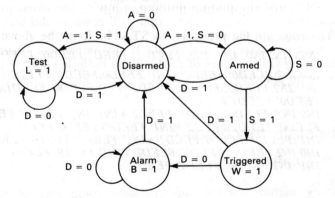

Fig. 5.7 State diagram for the burglar alarm example.

There are three inputs, a door sensor which detects intruders and a pair of switches to arm and disarm the system. If an attempt is made to arm the system with the door open, a warning light is turned on. Once armed, a buzzer will

57 / PLA based design

sound if the door is opened and, if a disarm signal is not received within one clock pulse, the bell will ring. The state diagram can be encoded in a language which is accepted by a program called STATIC which will automatically generate the Boolean equations required. [8] The encoded form of this diagram is shown below:

```
!!!!Static description of a burglar alarm!!!!
CONSTANTS
    on=1
    off=0
INPUTS
    Arm, Disarm, Sensor
OUTPUTS
    Bell, Light, Warning_buzzer
TABLE
    STATE Disarmed
        If Arm AND NOT Sensor GOTO Armed;
        If Arm AND Sensor      GOTO Test
                               DO Light=on;
        If NOT Arm             GOTO Disarmed;
    STATE Armed
        If Disarm              GOTO Disarmed;
        If Sensor AND NOT Disarm GOTO Triggered
                               DO Warning_buzzer=on;
        If NOT Sensor AND NOT Disarm GOTO Armed;
    STATE Triggered
        If Disarm              GOTO Disarmed;
        If NOT Disarm GOTO Alarm DO Bell=on;
    STATE Alarm
        If Disarm              GOTO Disarmed;
        If NOT Disarm GOTO Alarm DO Bell=on;
    STATE Test
        If Disarm              GOTO Disarmed;
        If NOT Disarm          GOTO Test
                               DO Light=on;
    !!!!!!!!!!!!!!!!!!!!!!!!!!!!!!!!!!!!!!!!!!!!!!!!!!
```

The equation file produced by STATIC from the above is

INPUTS: IN0, IN1, IN2, FEED 2, FEED1,FEED0; FEEDS: 3;

IN0.IN2.FEED0'.FEED2'+IN1'.FEED0.FEED1'.FEED2';
IN1'.IN2.FEED0'.FEED1'.FEED2+IN1'.FEED0'.FEED1.FEED2'+IN1'.
FEED0'.FEED1.FEED2;
IN0.IN2'.FEED0'.FEED1'.FEED2'+IN1'.IN2'.FEED0'.FEED1'.FEED2+IN1'.
FEED0'.FEED1.FEED2'+IN1'.FEED0'.FEED1.FEED2;
IN1'.FEED0'.FEED1.FEED2'+IN1'.FEED0'.FEED1.FEED2;
IN0.IN2.FEED0'.FEED1'.FEED2'+IN1'.FEED0.FEED1'.FEED2';
IN1'.IN2.FEED0'.FEED1'.FEED2;
⋮

When this is implemented, one state transition will take place each time the PLA is clocked, corresponding to one **IF..GOTO** line in the STATIC description. The states are encoded into the minimum number of bits required. STATIC does not, however, minimize the logic equations for the FSM.

5.6   Minimizing PLA size

There are basically four ways to reduce the size of a PLA; logic minimization, folding, partitioning and the use of special types of PLA structure.

5.6.1   LOGIC MINIMIZATION FOR PLAs

The minimizing of the equations must be done by multiple output minimization, where the goal is to minimize the total number of product terms rather than the number of AND/OR operations. [9] The size of a PLA is in fact fixed by the number of inputs m, the number of outputs n and the number of product terms p as

$$(\text{PLA area}) = (2m + n).p.(\text{basic cell size})$$

(neglecting buffers and other peripheral cells). Since m and n are fixed for a particular function, only p can be minimized.

Minimizing the equations by hand is tedious and unreliable for large PLAs; hence a CAD tool can be of use here. The PLAMIN program [10] takes a set of Boolean equations and produces a minimized version. The minimizer makes some compromises between final reduction and CPU time used. The output is in the form of a table which can be used by PLAGEN as shown in Section 5.3.2.

5.6.2   TOPOLOGICAL MINIMIZATION

It sometimes happens that the programming transistors in a PLA form a rather sparse matrix, as shown in Fig. 5.8a. When this occurs, some area reduction is possible by splitting up the PLA and removing the redundant parts, as shown in Fig. 5.8b. Since some pairs of product terms must share rows, this means that output must emerge from both sides of the AND plane and the OR plane must be split. By applying a similar method to the OR plane, the version in Fig. 5.8c is obtained, where some outputs appear at the top.

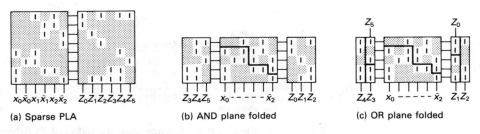

(a) Sparse PLA (b) AND plane folded (c) OR plane folded

Fig. 5.8   Stages in folding a PLA.

A disadvantage of this type of minimization is that it prevents the swapping of rows and columns of the PLA.

5.6.3 PARTITIONING

Often, a particular function such as controlling a CPU will produce a PLA which is very large. By partitioning the function and using several smaller PLAs it is often possible to reduce the total area used. For example, the CPU controller could be split into a main control sequencer, an ALU function decoder, a shift function decoder and so on.

Attempts have been made to partition functions automatically, but it seems likely that some knowledge of the overall nature of the problem is needed to obtain the best reduction, hence it is best done by the designer.

5.6.4 SPECIAL PURPOSE PLA STRUCTURES

Variations on the simple AND–OR PLA can be used to optimize the PLA for a particular function. Functions which use exclusive-or operations such as parity checks and addition are particularly inefficient in the simple PLA. By adding an extra level of logic (an extra plane) to produce a NOR–NOR–NOR PLA or by doing some decoding of groups of inputs to the AND plane, it is possible to improve the efficiency in terms of size. The graphs in Fig. 5.9 are derived from statistics collected by Sasao [11] and show that the improvement is more significant for parity type functions.

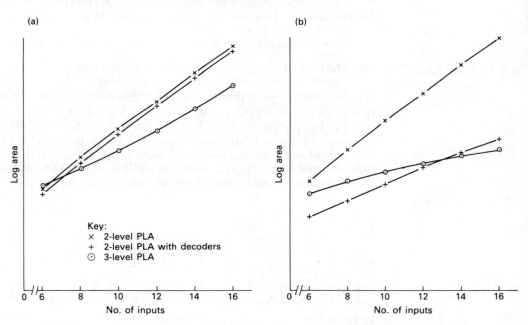

Fig. 5.9 Comparison of average size for different PLA types: (a) arbitrary functions; (b) parity functions.

Another special case is the adder PLA devised by Weinberger [12] which uses both input decoders and exclusive-or gates at the outputs to produce large adders.

5.7 Conclusions

The PLA is a useful object for implementing combinational and sequential logic using a full custom fabrication process. It is possible to start from a state table or Boolean equation description of the required function and produce the mask data automatically, making this a fast and reliable design technique. It lies somewhere between the gate array and custom cell design in terms of speed of operation, design effort and flexibility. With the appropriate CAD tools, PLA based design is a very competitive method for the design of application specific integrated circuits.

References

1. Barna, A. and Porat, D.I. *Integrated Circuits in Digital Electronics*. Wiley-Interscience (1973), p. 43.
2. *VLSI Design Tools Manual V1.9*. Department of Electrical and Electronic Engineering, Newcastle University (1983).
3. Hon, R.W. and Sequin, C.H. A guide to LSI implementation. 2nd edition, Xerox PARC/SSL, *Tech. Report SSL-79-7*, Palo Alto, California (1980).
4. Hodges, D.A. and Jackson, H.G. *Analysis and Design of Integrated Circuits*. McGraw-Hill International Student Edition (1983), p. 416.
5. Glasser, L.A. and Song, W.S. *Introductory CMOS Techniques*. VLSI Memo No. 82-117, Massachusetts Institute of Technology (1983).
6. Kohavi, Z. *Switching and Finite Automata Theory*, 2nd Edition. McGraw-Hill (1970), p. 275 *et seq*.
7. Mead, C.A. and Conway, L.A. *Introduction to VLSI Systems*. Addison-Wesley (1980), p. 82.
8. Morris, D.T. *Design, Implementation and Application of an Automated Controller Design System*. Computer Science Dept., Leeds University (1982).
9. Friedman, A.D. and Menon, P.R. *Theory and Design of Switching Circuits*. Computer Science Press, Maryland (1975), p. 65 *et seq*.
10. Lim, C.Y. *A PLA Minimiser Program*. Final year student thesis, Dept. of Electrical and Electronic Engineering, University of Newcastle Upon Tyne (1982).
11. Sasao, T. Multiple-valued decomposition of generalised Boolean functions and the complexity of programmable logic arrays. *IEEE Trans. Comp.* **C-30**(9) (1981).
12. Weiberger, A. High speed programmable logic array adders. *IBM J. Res. Development*, **23**(2), 163-179 (1979).

6 Simulation

6.1 Introduction

In the design of complex digital sysems the major issues of design verification and test vector generation require that a model of the system, both under faulty and fault free conditions, be created, the model to be exercised with some input stimuli, and the output response of the system to the input stimuli predicted by the model. This three-stage process is called simulation.

During the design of a digital system, the simulation process is carried out at several levels of abstraction, each level yielding information on different aspects of the design. The higher levels of simulation are used to check the functional aspects of the system design, whereas the lower levels relate to design aspects associated with performance and physical implementation. As one descends through the levels of abstraction signal representations change from character representations to discrete logic levels and then to quasi-continuous voltage levels; in a similar way events, i.e. changes in signal values, are expressed as a number of clock cycles at the higher levels and as submultiples of seconds at the lower levels.

The levels of simulation which may be used in the design process are

(1) behavioural level;
(2) register transfer level;
(3) functional level;
(4) gate level;
(5) switch level;
(6) timing level;
(7) circuit level;
(8) device level.

In general the designer is not involved with device level [1] simulation, since this is used to examine various aspects of the fabrication process on device parameters, for example, threshold voltage, junction capacitance.

6.2 Applications of simulation

In the design process simulation has a wide range of applications, it may be used for the following:

(1) *Function verification*. In this mode the designer uses the simulator to verify that the system or part of a system performs the desired function; for example, if an up–down counter was part of a system, then a gate-level model of the counter would be described to the simulator and the basic functions of the counter, that is incrementing, decrementing, clearing to zero, etc. would be verified by the simulator.

(2) *Fault simulation*. A necessary adjunct to test vector generation is fault simulation, in order to determine the number of faults detected by the test vectors. The three techniques currently used for fault simulation are parallel fault simulation, deductive fault simulation and concurrent fault simulation (Section 6.5).

(3) *Spike and hazard analysis*. An important application of simulation is that of monitoring switching anomalies which may occur anywhere in the circuit and cause the circuit to malfunction. This simulation function is normally performed at gate level and the designer usually has the ability to define to the simulator the minimum acceptable width of a pulse on the output of a gate; if it is less than this value it is deemed to be an unwanted 'spike'.

(4) *Timing analysis*. In addition to verifying that a circuit functions correctly, the designer is also interested in the various delays which exist in the circuit and how these may affect the performance. Thus the designer may perform a timing analysis on parts of a circuit whose delays may be deemed critical to the operation of the circuit.

(5) *Sensitivity analysis*. In the design style which configures systems from a library of predefined cells, it is necessary to determine, for example, how the switching levels and propagation characteristics of the cells vary with temperature. Consequently, during a circuit level simulation of the cell, the circuit component values can be made temperature sensitive, hence the effects of temperature upon the circuit performance can be observed.

(6) *Evaluation of design alternatives*. During the initial phases of conceptual design of a system, simulation allows the designer to examine, readily, design alternatives which may, for example, improve the performance of the system or enhance the testability of the system.

6.3 Types of simulator

6.3.1 CIRCUIT LEVEL SIMULATOR [2]

Circuit level simulation is generally the lowest level used in the design of digital systems: early reference to circuit simulation invariably uses the term 'circuit analysis'. The aims of using circuit simulation in digital system design are to determine the electrical performance characteristics of a group of transistors, which may be considered at a higher level of abstraction to be a logic gate, and to analyse circuits which have tightly coupled feedback loops or circuits where analogue voltage levels are important. Circuit level simulation is usually performed on a few tens of transistors, requiring ten to fifteen minutes of CPU time; however, it has been known in industry to use circuit simulation on complete systems comprising several thousand transistors, requiring many tens of hours of CPU time, in order to establish the reason for a malfunction in a new circuit design.

Although circuit simulators are capable of performing both a.c. and d.c. linear and non-linear analysis and transient analysis, their use in digital system design is mainly limited to d.c. and transient analysis. The circuit to be analysed is described to the simulator using a special purpose circuit description language which defines the type of component, its value and its connections; active devices usually have additional statements which may define, for example, its physical dimensions, device capacitances, etc. The circuit description language also provides a means of describing input waveforms to the circuit and terminal supply voltages. An example of a simple circuit description using SPICE [3] is shown in Fig. 6.1. Within the simulator the electrical behaviour of the components is represented by a mathematical model defined in terms of ideal components. At circuit level the quantities of interest are currents and voltages as a function of time. The procedure [4] for calculating the values of currents and voltages begins by formulating the circuit equations using either modified nodal anlaysis or sparse tableau techniques [5]; thereafter, if a linear d.c. analysis is required, a Gaussian elimination technique is used to solve the matrix equations; if a non-linear d.c. analysis is required the Newton–Raphson technique is used to convert the non-linear equations into a set of linear equations to be solved by Gaussian elimination; if a transient analysis is required this is performed using implicit numerical integration techniques.

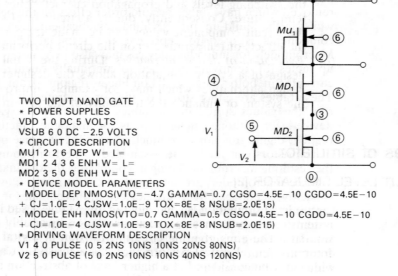

TWO INPUT NAND GATE
* POWER SUPPLIES
VDD 1 0 DC 5 VOLTS
VSUB 6 0 DC −2.5 VOLTS
* CIRCUIT DESCRIPTION
MU1 2 2 6 DEP W= L=
MD1 2 4 3 6 ENH W= L=
MD2 3 5 0 6 ENH W= L=
* DEVICE MODEL PARAMETERS
. MODEL DEP NMOS(VTO= −4.7 GAMMA=0.7 CGSO=4.5E−10 CGDO=4.5E−10
+ CJ=1.0E−4 CJSW=1.0E−9 TOX=8E−8 NSUB=2.0E15)
. MODEL ENH NMOS(VTO=0.7 GAMMA=0.5 CGSO=4.5E−10 CGDO=4.5E−10
+ CJ=1.0E−4 CJSW=1.0E−9 TOX=8E−8 NSUB=2.0E15)
* DRIVING WAVEFORM DESCRIPTION
V1 4 0 PULSE (0 5 2NS 10NS 10NS 20NS 80NS)
V2 5 0 PULSE (5 0 2NS 10NS 10NS 40NS 120NS)

Fig. 6.1 Example of a circuit description using SPICE.

In order to compare the salient features of the different levels of simulation, Table A.1 in the Appendix to this chapter lists the essential characteristics of a circuit level simulator. It should be noted that in Table A.1 and all subsequent tables in the Appendix, the list of existing programs is by no means exhaustive and is simply a representative sample of the more common programmes.

6.3.2 TIMING LEVEL SIMULATOR [6]

In comparison to circuit simulation, timing level simulation is a relatively new addition to the arsenal of simulation tools. In the mid-1970s, with the design of relatively complex circuits, several new design problems resulting from the design techniques and technology used had to be examined; these problems — namely clock breakthrough and charge sharing — are related to the electrical behaviour of the circuit; circuit simulation, although capable of simulating these effects, was too inefficient with respect to CPU time and memory storage, whilst gate level simulation, which can simulate large circuits more efficiently than circuit level, uses a model which is at too high a level to simulate the electrical behaviour of the circuit. Consequently a level of simulation, timing level, had to be introduced which would not only be cost effective in simulating large LSI circuits but also have ability to simulate electrical circuit behaviour with an accuracy comparable to circuit level simulation.

Timing level simulation is much more efficient than circuit level because it uses simpler models and relaxed simulation methods. The simulation models used are called macromodels [7], which model only the terminal behaviour of a device and hence reduce model evaluation time, which accounts for approximately 85% of the analysis time in a circuit level simulation. The macromodels can either be created by a 'simplification' process or a 'build-up' process. In the 'simplification' process a circuit model of a device has elements removed which have only a second order effect on the behaviour of the device, whilst in the 'build-up' process a mathematical equation or a small assembly of components is used to represent the terminal behaviour of the device. Macromodels for individual devices may also be generated in the form of look-up tables [8], removing the need to continually calculate the values of device currents, in both linear and non-linear regions, from the model equations. These tables are either stored on disk or generated at the start of a simulation run; the values stored in the tables can usually be scaled, depending upon device size. Although macromodels for analogue functions can be generated readily, digital functions are much more difficult, since in MOS designs groups of transistors can readily be assembled to perform complex logical functions, the resulting macromodel being as complex as the original device configuration.

Since macromodels are simpler than circuit models, usually because internal capacitive feedback effects are neglected, inaccuracies in the simulation results will exist, but these may be reduced if macromodels are used to represent larger functions than single devices. The accuracy obtained from a timing simulator using macromodels is approximately 85–90% of the value obtained from a circuit level simulation of a given circuit, with, however, a much reduced simulation time.

In the timing simulator the increase in performance is achieved not only by using simpler models but also by exploiting the latency which exists in all digital circuits, i.e. periods during which the circuit is inactive. Since the values of electrical variables are constant during these periods no computational effort is required, thus reducing the analysis time. In order to exploit circuit latency it is necessary to identify nodes which will be inactive during analysis time; this can only be done satisfactorily if, as in macromodels, the input and output nodes are essentially isolated and not linked by any internal capacitive feedback paths which exist in circuit models, inhibiting latency exploitation in circuit level simulation.

The essential characteristics of a timing level simulator are shown in Table A.2.

6.3.3 SWITCH LEVEL SIMULATORS [9]

This level of simulation evolved as an inexpensive way of realizing a logic level simulator, whilst at the same time, due to the inherent simplicity of the simulation primitives, being able to evaluate MOS circuits containing device configurations which proved troublesome to conventional gate/logic level simulators.

The features of MOS circuits which make them difficult to simulate using conventional gate level simulators are the bilateral switching characteristic of MOS devices, the inherent data storage capability of isolated nodes in the circuits and the ability to group MOS transistors together to perform complex logic functions which cannot be readily realized using standard logic functions.

In a switch level simulator the basic primitive is a MOS device modelled as a voltage controlled switch having, in general, no preferred direction for signal transmission; this is in contrast to gate level primitives which inherently exhibit a unilateral switching characteristic. At switch level, although the circuit is assumed to comprise a series of nodes connected by transistors, it is emphasized that the transistors are regarded as ideal switches and not analogue devices as at circuit level; consequently circuits comprising thousands of devices can be simulated readily without incurring excessive simulation run times. Furthermore, since the simulation primitives correspond to the basic active elements used in the layout, the circuit description for the simulator can be extracted directly from the layout without any reference to the intended function of the circuit, thus enabling the designer to verify that the layout does realize the intended function, without the translation from layout to some suitable simulation configuration being biased by an *a priori* knowledge of the circuit function.

At switch level, a three-valued signal representation (0,1 and don't care) is used when analysing the circuit. The classic high-impedance state normally used at gate level when simulating pass transistors is not used at switch level, since the high-impedance state is inherently produced by the simulation primitive used. Although the basic simulation primitive is the MOS transistor, in the interest of efficiency, most switch level simulators permit predefined logic elements in the circuit description: for example, inverters, NAND and NOR gates. The simulation algorithm used at switch level has been referred to as a 'dynamic topology algorithm' since at each evaluation of the circuit a new signal-flow model of the circuit is created to simulate the effects of input logic changes, the connections between nodes being opened or closed depending upon the logic values applied to the gate terminals of the MOS devices. The evaluation of the signal nodes is iterated until a consistent set of logic values is obtained.

The essential characteristics of a switch level simulator are summarized in Table A.3.

6.3.4 GATE LEVEL SIMULATOR [10, 11]

Gate level simulation marks the change in signal level representaton from quasi-continuous voltage levels to discrete logic levels. Within the strict definition of a gate level simulator, that is one in which the only simulation primitives are NAND, AND, OR and NOR gates, few gate level simulators exist; one example, however, is D-lasar. [12] Most so called gate-level simulators have the capability of simulating higher-level functions such as flip flops and shift registers, and so they fall into the class of functional level simulators.

In a gate level simulator it is the logical behaviour of a group of active devices realizing a given gate function which is modelled. A gate model comprises two components: the first is an ideal gate whose logic function may be represented either by a 'look-up' table, which is essentially a truth table, or by a program which examines each input to the gate in turn in an attempt to identify the output logic value of the gate. The output of the ideal gate is then fed to the input of the second component of the gate model — namely, a delay block which is used to simulate the various delay parameters associated with the gate. The number of logic levels used in a gate model ranges from two to nine, although simulators exist which use fifteen levels to represent the activity on the output node of a gate. Obviously the more levels used to represent transitions on a gate output and the more complex the delay model, the more accurate are the simulation results, with a corresponding increase in CPU time due to the increase in sophistication of the gate evaluation routines.

Gate level simulation has a speed advantage over circuit level simulation by at least two orders of magnitude and is capable of efficiently simulating circuits of complexities of the order of 20 000 gates/flip flops. The increase in speed of simulation at gate level is obtained by using simpler simulation models which do not require the formulation of circuit equations and their subsequent solution. Gate level simulators also exploit the unilateral switching characteristics of most logic functions, i.e. signal propagation is always performed from input to output. Furthermore gate level simulators exploit to the highest degree the structural and temporal sparsity characteristics of digital circuits.

The main applications of gate level simulators are as follows:

(1) Verification of the logical behaviour of a circuit. Hence the simulator must be capable as simulating both combinational and sequential (asynchronous and synchronous) circuits.

(2) Detection of switching anomalies in the circuit.

(3) Determination of the fault coverage for a set of test vectors.

(4) Test vector verification, since test vectors usually exercise a circuit in a way which was not intended. Consequently, spikes or glitches may be generated due to delays in the circuit, nullifying the test vector, which is usually generated without any consideration of circuit delays, particularly in sequential circuits. [13]

(5) Determination of logic assignments to gate inputs during automatic test vector generation. [14]

To illustrate the effects that the different signal value representations have, at each level of abstraction, on the aspects of circuit behaviour which can be observed, consider the application of both a gate level and circuit level simulator, first to examine the effect of increasing the fanout of a gate on the output voltage, and second to detect glitches.

Using a circuit simulator, as the gate fanout is increased it may be observed that the gate output voltage drops until it is unable to drive the gate inputs on its fanout. However, with a gate level simulator, since we are concerned with a behavioural model, there is no limit to the drive capability of a gate unless it is specified in the simulation package that, say, for a given technology the maximum fanout per gate must not exceed some defined value.

The generation of spikes or glitches on the output node of a logic gate is essentially a behavioural problem and consequently their detection is not catered for at circuit level. Glitches or spikes can be detected only from a circuit simulation by the visual inspection of node voltage waveforms displayed in the simulation results. Furthermore, the use of small time steps during a simulation run renders automatic glitch detection at circuit level inefficient. However, at gate level, since discrete logic levels are used for signal representation and also since time increments are controlled by events in the circuit, it is relatively easy to include a glitch detection routine in the gate simulation models, permitting glitches to be detected on all nodes in the circuit and not limited to those displayed in the simulation results.

The salient features of gate level simulators are summarized in Table A.4.

6.3.5 BEHAVIOURAL LEVEL SIMULATOR [15]

The concept of behavioural level simulation is that of creating and exercising a model of a system/function which characterizes the input/output behaviour of the system/function without specific reference to its internal structure. Although the term behavioural level simulation is usually associated with a high-level abstraction of a system, it can equally well be applied to a gate level simulation of say a three-input NAND gate in comparison to its circuit model, since at gate level we are essentially concerned with the terminal behaviour of the NAND gate.

In its commonly accepted sense, behavioural level simulation evolved from the need of the designer to have a more abstract representation of the system which was being designed. Gate level and higher functional block level primitives, i.e. flip flops and counters, etc., were too low a level of representation for complex systems, resulting in long simulation times, which produced excessive amounts of output data and also required a vast amount of input data.

Several approaches to behavioural simulation have been adopted. First, the customized simulation program: where a program written in a high-level language is generated for each circuit; this technique requires that the designer is also an efficient programmer and has the disadvantage that each simulation program must be debugged. Its main advantage, however, is that it offsets the cost of developing a general purpose simulator. However, most behavioural level simulation is performed using a general purpose simulator in which the system to be simulated is described using a range of built-in high level functions or by using functional modelling language [16]; the main advantage of using a functional modelling language is that it eliminates the necessity of updating the function library in the simulator.

Behavioural level simulation offers several advantages: first, the input description is essentially a system specification against which the performance of lower-level specifications can be compared; second, conceptual design faults can be detected earlier in the design cycle, since the designer is concerned only with the terminal behaviour of five or six functional blocks; third, simulation is more efficient since one event at behavioural level may be equated, for example, to one hundred events at gate level.

The essential characteristics of a behavioural level simulator are summarized in Table A.5.

6.3.6 MIXED MODE SIMULATOR [17]

Mixed mode simulation permits sections of a digital system to be simulated, concurrently, at different levels of abstraction. An example of a circuit where mixed mode simulation may be used is in the design of a random access memory, where the memory array may be simulated at behavioural level, the row and column decoders at gate level, the buffers at timing level and the sense amplifiers at circuit level. Mixed mode simulation may also be used in situations where it is necessary to examine a critical timing path through a circuit without decomposing the complete circuit to the level where timing simulation can be performed. At the outset mixed mode simulation was limited to the lower levels of simulation, i.e. gate, timing and circuit, but now the higher levels of abstraction have been integrated into mixed mode simulators [18]; this has the advantage that individual modules in a high-level description can be replaced by a more detailed representation, thus easing the problem of locating errors in the design, since if only one module is replaced and the system does not function correctly it implies that either the lower-level representation is incorrect or the interface between functions is incorrect. Furthermore the ability to interface behavioural descriptions, say with gate level models, permits models of low-level functions, for example bilateral transfer gates, to be included in a simulator without involving the software support needed to incorporate such functions into a library. Another application of mixed mode simulation is the generation of the driving waveforms to exercise a given module decomposed to a lower level of abstraction. In the past the designer would have to derive, manually, the input signals to a given module, from the overall operation of the system. However, if mixed mode simulation is used the inputs to the lower level functions will be generated automatically from the normal inputs to the circuit and the higher-level function blocks.

Mixed mode simulation, however, has the disadvantage that when levels of abstraction are merged, signals which cross from the discrete logic domain to the continuous voltage domain must pass through interface blocks which perform a logic to voltage conversion and vice versa. At present, it is necessary, when performing a mixed mode simulation, to describe each section of the circuit in terms of the simulation primitives appropriate to that level of abstraction, and also to insert the appropriate interface modules.

Table A.6 summarizes the essential characteristics of a mixed mode simulator.

6.4 Basic components of a simulator

A simulator, in general, comprises four modules: first, a *preprocessor module* which checks the syntax of the language used to describe the circuit to be simulated to the computer; second, a *model compiler* which transforms the input circuit description into some internal representation upon which the simulator executive operates; third, the *simulator executive*, which essentially controls the running of the simulator, services simulation control commands, and evaluates signal changes in the circuit; finally, a *display-processor module* which formats and displays the simulation results to the user's requirements.

The implementation of the pre-processor and display module functions in all types of simulator are very similar, however, the model compiler and simulator executive, although they perform the same general function, their implementation differs considerably, depending upon the level of simulation. For example consider the particular functions of the model complier and simulator executive in the circuit level and the gate level simulators.

In the circuit level simulator the model compiler generates a set of simultaneous equations, which is the internal representation or model of the circuit at that level. The section of the simulator executive concerned with signal evaluation comprises a set of routines to solve these equations. In the gate level simulator, however, the model compiler may generate a set of tables interlinked with pointers to represent the circuit to be simulated. The signal evaluation section of the simulator executive comprises a set of routines which define the output logic value of a gate knowing the type of gate and input logic values.

6.4.1 ARCHITECTURE OF A GATE LEVEL SIMULATOR

In the previous section the basic components of a simulator were discussed in general. As a specific example, let us consider these components in relation to a gate level simulator and also describe the simulation mechanisms which were developed to improve simulation efficiency at gate level and which have now been adopted at other levels of simulation.

6.4.2 PREPROCESSOR

The initial task to be performed when simulating a circuit is to describe the circuit topology to the computer, and this is done using a special purpose language. In practice there are numerous languages used to describe a circuit at gate level; however, in essence, each language describes a gate by specifying its function, assigning a unique name to its output and listing input signal names to the gate. The order of the inputs is usually irrelevant, except where an input performs a specific function; for example, in a D-type flip flop, there are inputs for data, clock, preset and clear, so these must be listed in a specific order as defined in the syntax of the language. The interconnections between gates/function are defined implicitly, since if a signal is found in a given input list it implies that a connection exists between the source of this signal and the gate input. An example of two gate description languages is shown below and describe a NAND gate, which has three inputs *IN1*, *IN2* and *IN3* and whose output signal is called *OUT1*.

OUT1 = NAND (IN1, IN2, IN3)

NAND OUT1 IN1 IN2 IN3

In addition to specifying the gates/functions in a circuit the special purpose languages also have the ability to describe the input/driving waveforms to the circuit. The waveforms may be repetitive, for example clock signals, or non-repetitive, describing input data or control signals. The format of the waveform description languages are again quite numerous, but essentially they classify the waveform as repetitive or non-repetitive, assign a unique identifier to the waveform, specify whether it starts on a high or low value and thereafer specify the times at which the waveform changes value; if the waveform is repetitive it is only necessary to define the transition times in the first cycle, and thereafter the program will generate the next cycles of the waveform automatically.

At gate level the circuit description can be large and inevitably will contain errors. Consequently, before the circuit is simulated the input description is passed through a preprocessor module whose function is to check that the circuit description is syntactically correct: i.e. valid gate/functions have been defined, each output has been assigned a unique name and the number of fan-ins per gate has not been exceeded. When the complete circuit description has been entered a check is made to ensure that the maximum fanout per gate has not been exceeded and that gates which have not been defined as primary outputs have at least one internal connection to another gate input. The preprocessor, however, will not detect the erroneous connections of signals in the circuit, i.e. signal A being connected to gate B rather than gate C; this type of error is detected by the designer only after the simulation has been run and the output waveforms are seen to be incorrect.

In some simulators, in order to reduce the tedium of producing the description of complex circuits comprising many identical functional blocks, for example decoders or multiplexers, the circuit description language contains a macro facility which permits a function to be described in detail with dummy input/output identifiers in a macro definition and thereafter instanced in the circuit description through a macro call, which assigns specific names to the dummy inputs/output identifiers. The macro calls are subsequently replaced with the detailed function description contained in the macro definition by the preprocessor module.

6.4.3 MODEL COMPILER

From the syntactically correct circuit description an internal representation or model of the circuit to be simulated is created by the model compiler. At gate level this model can be in the form of either a series of computer instructions, in which case the simulator is referred to as a *compiled code simulator*, or a set of interlinked tables, in which case it is referred to as a *table driven simulator*.

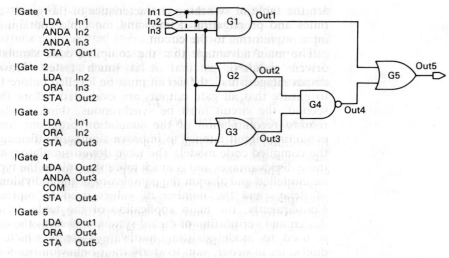

```
!Gate 1
      LDA   In1
      ANDA  In2
      ANDA  In3
      STA   Out1
!Gate 2
      LDA   In2
      ORA   In3
      STA   Out2
!Gate 3
      LDA   In1
      ORA   In2
      STA   Out3
!Gate 4
      LDA   Out2
      ANDA  Out3
      COM
      STA   Out4
!Gate 5
      LDA   Out1
      ORA   Out4
      STA   Out5
```

Fig. 6.2 Compiled code model of a circuit.

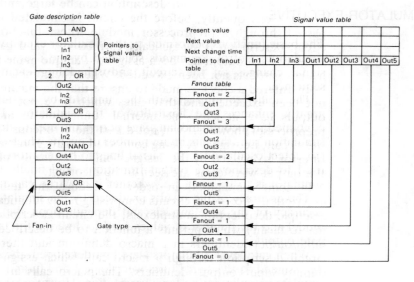

Fig. 6.3 Table driven data structure for the circuit in Fig. 6.2.

An example of the compiled code model of a circuit is shown in Fig. 6.2 and the corresponding table driven model is shown in Fig. 6.3. The compiled code model is essentially a computer program comprising groups of instructions which will simulate the logic function of the gates in the circuit; consequently, if the circuit is modified the simulation program must be recompiled. This is in contrast to the table driven simulator, where the circuit model is considered as the input data to a simulation program which is the same for all circuits. In the example of the table driven simulator shown in Fig. 6.3, only the main tables and associated pointers are shown; some of the tables which have been omitted are the table of switching characteristics of the gates, containing rise and fall times and propagation delays, and the table containing a description of the input waveforms to the circuit.

The main advantage that the compiled code simulator has over the table driven simulator is that it is much faster. However, it has several disadvantages: first, the circuit must be levelled before the model is generated, to ensure that all gate outputs are evaluated before they are used as inputs; second, the circuit must be synchronous; third, modifications to the circuit require recompilation of the simulation program; fourth, the technique of exploiting circuit latency to improve simulator efficiency cannot be applied to the compiled code model. The table driven simulator, however, does not have these disadvantages and is much more versatile in the types of circuits which can be modelled and also on the complexity of the individual gate models, in terms of delays and the number of values used to represent signal transitions. Consequently, the main application of the table driven simulator is in the design and verification of digital systems, whereas the compiled code simulator is used to model existing hardware systems which are too expensive to duplicate, in order, say, to study their behaviour under some fault condition.

6.4.4 SIMULATOR EXECUTIVE

The basic functions performed by the simulator executive are implementing the simulation control commands specified by the user, evaluating the effects of signal changes on the circuit and scheduling events in the correct time sequence.

The ability to interact with the simulator by way of a command language greatly enhances the flexibility of the simulator. The directives typically contained in a command language permit the user to define the duration of the simulation run, the maximum number of events which should occur in this time (to detect oscillations), the signal lines to be monitored, the number of values used to describe gate output transitions, and finally the mode in which the simulator is to be used, i.e. whether it is a true value or fault simulator.

The accuracy of the results produced by the simulator is determined by the accuracy of the gate models and depends upon the delays included in the model and the number of values used to describe the transitions occurring at a gate output.

When gate level simulators were first developed, the only values which could be assigned to the signal lines were logic 1 and 0, and thus the function of the simulator was limited to logic verification. However, the introduction of a third value, an X or unknown state, greatly increased the usefulness of the simulator. First, the presence of switching anomalies [19] could be detected in the circuit, since if a gate switched from, say a logic 1, to an X-state, and then back to a logic 1, it would indicate that a glitch was present in the circuit. Second, at the start of a simulation run, if all gates are initialized to an X-state, then the propagation delay time through the circuit can be determined. Third, by setting the outputs of registers to an X-state, the ability to set/reset the registers from any initial value can be checked with only one simulation pass. The number of values which could be assigned to signal lines, subsequently, was increased to four, since some designers wished to be more specific about the significance of the X-state, wishing to differentiate between an X-state assigned to a gate output at the beginning of a simulation run and an X-state produced at a gate output as a result of a switching anomaly. Other four-valued simulators, rather than considering two different X-states, introduced a high-impedance value, which is necessary when simulating circuits containing transmission gates. To date, the number of values used to describe the condition existing on a gate output ranges from three through to fifteen; however, as the number of values assigned to a signal line increases, the decision about which value to assign to a gate output becomes more complex and requires some order of precedence to be assigned to the gate input values. The usual convention is that the most pessimistic value dominates unless an input value exists which can categorically define the output value on the gate.

Since simulation is the calculation of logic values as a function of time, delays which exist in the actual circuit must be included in the gate models. These are as follows:

(1) *Transport delay*. Each gate or connection that a signal passes through must introduce a time delay, which is referred to as the transport delay and is usually represented as a pure delay block on the output of a gate.

(2) *Ambiguity delay*. Since the exact delays through a gate are not always known, a pair of delays are assigned to the gate defining a time window when it is uncertain whether a gate transition has occurred or not.

(3) *Rise and fall delays*. When a gate changes state it does not affect the change immediately due to capacitances in the circuit. Consequently, gate transitions have a rise or fall time. In general since these two delays are not equal the width of the output pulse is distorted.

(4) *Inertial delays*. If the width of a dominant input pulse to a gate is very short, it will not force the device to switch. The minimum duration that a logic change must remain on an input before the gate responds is called the inertial delay time of the gate. If the pulse width is greater that the inertial delay time, the effect of the inertial delay is similar to that of the transport delay; otherwise the input pulse is suppressed.

Gate models can either have zero, unit, assignable or precise delays.

The mechanism for scheduling events, i.e. gate changes, during simulation can be carried out either by using a 'next event list processing' algorithm, which assumes that events can occur asynchronously during the simulation, or by using a 'time mapping' algorithm which restricts the occurrence of events to multiples of some fixed time increment.

Next event list processing

This technique comprises setting up a simple list structure in which events are ordered with increasing time. The list must be continually processed to ensure that events are entered into the list in the correct time sequence, otherwise mis-scheduling of events will occur. If the list is long, implying that there is much activity in the circuit, time is wasted in processing the list. The advantages of this technique are that it is easy to implement, the advancement of time is accomplished by jumping from one scheduled event to another, and finally, there are no constraints on times when events can occur.

Time mapping event scheduling technique [20]

In this technique, shown in Fig. 6.4, a circular loop (Δt loop) is used to represent time, each sector in the table represents a time increment of Δt. The time increment and the number of sectors in the loop are determined prior to the start of the simulation from the circuit delays. During the simulation each sector will contain either a signal name or a pointer to list of signal names which will change state at that time. Future events are scheduled into the appropriate time slot by adding the gate delay, expressed in terms of Δt, onto the current pointer position in the loop. Consequently, there is no need to scan the event list in order to schedule future events. In this technique time is incremented by stepping around the sectors in the loop. This process can be inefficient in circuits where there is a large difference between the smallest and the greatest delays in the circuit and the activity in the circuit is sparse: this results in a loop with a large number of small sectors many of which will not contain a scheduled event. Time, however, can only be advanced a sector at a time, thus time is wasted in scanning the empty sectors. In this situation, an attempt to use a time loop whose length is less than the maximum delay in the circuit will result in events being mis-scheduled. Efficient time scheduling can be obtained in these situations if two loops are used, as shown in Fig. 6.5, in

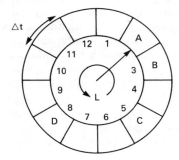

Fig. 6.4   Time mapping event scheduling technique.

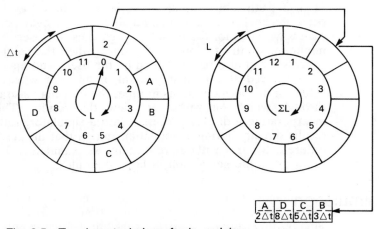

Fig. 6.5   Two loop technique for long delays.

which case the increment on the first loop is Δt and its length represents some delay which is smaller than the maximum circuit delay, whilst the increment on the second loop is the length of the first loop. After each rotation of the small loop, a pointer to the large loop is incremented by one and the events scheduled for this time period, as shown, are loaded into the small loop, and the sectors of the small loop are scanned as before.

Exploitation of latency

As the size of the circuit to be simulated increases there is a corresponding increase in CPU time; consequently techniques had to be developed to improve simulation efficiency. The first technique to be developed was the event driven simulator, where signal evaluation in the circuit is initiated by the occurrence of an event as indicated by the event scheduling algorithm using the next-event list processing technique; hence gate evaluation of the circuit during inactive periods is avoided. The efficiency of the simulators was further increased when it was noted that when signals changed logic value at some instant in time, these changes would affect only a small percentage of the gates in the circuit — namely, the gates in the fanout lists of the signals lines which changed value. Consequently, in order to determine the effect of the signal changes on the circuit at a given time, it is only necessary to evaluate the changes in logic state on those gates which are in the fanout list of the signal lines which changed state. This simulation technique is known as *selective trace* and can only be applied to circuits where the gates exhibit a unilateral switching characteristic. In circuits which have bilateral switching devices, it is necessary to partition the circuit into modules, where the interconnections between the modules are unidirectional; thereafter the technique of selective trace simulation can be applied.

6.4.5 DISPLAY PROCESSOR

The display processor comprises a set of editing commands which permit the user to display the simulation results in a format which is most appropriate to his requirements. The simulation results may be displayed as set of waveforms or in a truth table format where signal values may be expressed in binary, octal, decimal or hexadecimal numbers. The display editor may also be used to scan waveforms for the presence of glitches, the user, beforehand, defining the minimum width of a pulse. The times when the results are displayed by the processor can also be controlled by the user, who may specify that the results are displayed at a regular interval of time, or when a given signal changes value, or at specific instants in time, the user may also define the time window through which he wishes to view the results. The main advantage of incorporating a display processor into a simulator, rather than producing the results directly during a simulation run, is that the results can be displayed in different formats without re-running the simulator. The penalty to be paid, however, is the generation of large data files.

6.5 Fault simulation

The class of simulators discussed in the preceding sections is referred to as 'true-value simulators' in that they predict the response of the circuit under fault-free conditions. Another class of simulators called 'fault' simulators are used extensively to predict the behaviour of the circuit under fault conditions. Fault simulators are used in conjunction with automatic test pattern generation programs: first, to determine the overall fault coverage of a set of test vectors; second, to determine what other faults a given test vector will detect, since the generation of a test for a fault condition is a time-consuming process, so that when a test vector is generated a fault simulator is used to determine what other faults the test will detect, since this is considered more economical than test vector generation.

In the past fault simulation was implemented by incorporating, into a true-value simulator, the ability to hold a gate output at a constant logic value, to simulate either a stuck-at-1 or stuck-at-0 fault; each test vector was then applied in turn and the output response of the circuit was predicted and compared with the fault-free circuit response. If these differed, then the test vector was able to detect the given fault condition. As circuit complexities increased this technique became very inefficient, and hence more efficient fault simulation techniques were developed:

(1) parallel fault simulation;
(2) deductive fault simulation;
(3) concurrent fault simulation.

To date the most common fault simulators commercially available use either the parallel or concurrent fault simulation techniques.

6.5.1 PARALLEL FAULT SIMULATION [21]

In parallel fault simulation N copies of a circuit are simulated in parallel, one fault-free circuit (reference) and $N-1$ faulty circuits. The number of faulty circuits which can be simulated in parallel depends upon the length of the computer word, each bit position in the word being used to identify a particular fault in the circuit. Consequently if there are M faults to be simulated, the number of simulation runs per input test pattern is the smallest integer greater than $M/(N-1)$. The number of simulation passes can be reduced further if independent faults are simulated together, that is faults which do not affect a common part of the circuit. Thus, if the circuit has P outputs, then the number of simulation passes required is the smallest integer greater than $M/((N-1).P)$. This technique can only be used to advantage provided the circuit fanout is low and the groups of independent faults are readily identified.

The technique of parallel fault simulation exploits the fact that logical operations are performed by the computer on words rather than individual bits. To illustrate the process consider the circuit shown in Fig. 6.6.

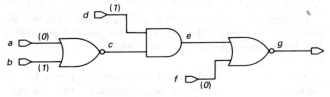

Fig. 6.6 Parallel fault simulation.

Each bit position represents a fault in the circuit. The method of performing a parallel fault simulation is as follows.

(1) Set up the input values for each version of the circuit; the underlined values (Table 6.1) representing the fault condition.
(2) Create new values for the internal nodes in the circuit by performing the logic functions indicated, inserting the given fault condition where appropriate.
(3) Continue (2) until the output is evaluated. The list of faults detected by a given test pattern is obtained by comparing the logic values in each bit position with the value in the reference position, those values which differ indicate the faults detected by the test vector.

It should be noted that in parallel fault simulation the faulty circuit is still simulated, although the faulty and fault free circuits produce the same response, this does not occur in the other methods of fault simulation.

Table 6.1

Bit position	0	1	2	3	4	5	6	7	8	9	10
Fault	Ref	a/1	b/0	c/1	c/0	d/0	e/1	e/0	f/1	g/1	g/0
	0	1	2	3	4	5	6	7	8	9	10
$a = 0$	0	1	0	0	0	0	0	0	0	0	0
$b = 1$	1	1	0	1	1	1	1	1	1	1	1
$c = \overline{a+b}$	0	0	1	1	0	0	0	0	0	0	0
$d = 1$	1	1	1	1	0	1	1	1	1	1	1
$e = c.d$	0	0	1	1	0	0	1	0	0	0	0
$f = 0$	0	0	0	0	0	0	0	0	1	0	0
$g = \overline{e+f}$	1	1	0	0	1	1	0	1	0	1	0

The faults detected by this input pattern, i.e. $a = f = 0$ and $b = d = 1$, are b stuck-at-0, c stuck-at-1, e stuck-at-1, f stuck-at-1 and g stuck-at-0.

6.5.2 DEDUCTIVE FAULT SIMULATION [22]

In the technique of deductive fault simulation only the fault free logic is simulated and from the current state of the good machine it is deduced which faults can be detected at an internal node or primary output of the circuit.

Since all detectable faults are determined at the same time it is only necessary to perform one simulation run per test vector; this is in contrast to the parallel fault simulation technique where $M/(N-1)$ passes per test vector were required.

In general, the time for a single simulation run of the deductive fault simulator is greater than that for the parallel simulator; however, it is less than the total time for the $M/(N-1)$ passes required by the parallel fault simulator for each test vector.

The deductive fault simulator does require a lot of memory which must be allocated dynamically to accommodate the varying size of the fault lists generated during the process.

The main step in deductive fault simulation is that of generating the fault lists which comprise,

(1) Faults detected at predecessor gates whose effect is propagated to the input of the given gate.

(2) Faults which originate at a given gate and produce an incorrect output at that gate for a given set of input conditions.

The rules used for deriving the fault lists are summarized below.

Consider an aribitrary Boolean function $F(X_1, X_2, \ldots, X_n)$ realized as either a sum of products or product of sums expression.

(1) If the value of X_i in the fault-free circuit is 0, replace all occurrences of X_i and $\bar{X}_i$ by L_{Xi} and $\bar{L}_{Xi}$ respectively, where L_{Xi} is the fault list associated with the signal line X_i.

(2) If the value of X_i in the fault free circuit is 1 replace all occurrences of X_i and $\bar{X}_i$ by $\bar{L}_{Xi}$ and L_{Xi} respectively.

(3) Replace the AND and OR operators in the function by the set operators $\cap$ and $\cup$ respectively.

(4) Simplify the fault list expressions using the set operations defined in (3).

(5) Append the appropriate stuck-at fault on the output of the function to the simplified fault list.

As an example of the deductive fault simulation technique consider the circuit shown in Fig. 6.6 and assuming, as in the example on parallel fault simulation, that the test vector applied to the inputs is $a = f = 0$ and $b = d = 1$.

Set up the fault lists for signals on inputs a and b; the only faults which can be detected on these inputs are a stuck-at-1, i.e. a_1, and b stuck-at-0, i.e. b_0.

Hence $L_a = \{a_1\}$; $L_b = \{b_0\}$

Propagate the fault lists through gate c. Initially

$$L_c = \{\overline{L_a \cup L_b}\} = \{\bar{L}_a \cap \bar{L}_b\} = b_0.$$

Append the fault condition on the output of gate c to the fault list, i.e. c stuck-at-1. That is,

$$L_c = \{b_0, c_1\}$$

Set up the fault list for input d, i.e. $L_d = \{d_0\}$.

Propagate fault lists through gate e.

Initially $L_e = \{L_c \cap \bar{L}_d\} = \{b_0, c_1\}$.

Append the fault condition on the output of gate e to the fault list, i.e. e stuck-at-1. That is,

$$L_e = \{b_0, c_1, e_1\}$$

Set up the fault condition for input f, i.e. $L_f = \{f_1\}$.

Propagate the fault lists through gate g.

Initially $L_g = \{\overline{L_e \cup L_f}\} = \{\bar{L}_e \cap \bar{L}_f\} = \{\bar{b}_0, c_1, e_1, f_1\}$.

However, since the true value of g is a logic 1, $L_g = \{b_0, c_1, e_1, f_1\}$.

Append the fault condition on the output of gate g to the fault list, e.g. 'g stuck-at-0'.

$$L_g = \{b_0, c_1, e_1, f_1, g_0\}.$$

6.5.3 CONCURRENT FAULT SIMULATION [23]

This technique combines the features of both parallel and deductive fault simulation. However, in concurrent fault simulation the faulty gates are only simulated when their output value differs from the fault free circuit value.

As an example of this technique consider the circuit shown in Fig. 6.7. Let input A have an s-a-1 fault, since for the given input conditions, the fault free and faulty circuits will have different output values, and consequently both circuits are simulated. If, however, input A changes to a logic 1, the faulty gate simulation ceases. A more detailed example of this method is shown in Fig. 6.8.

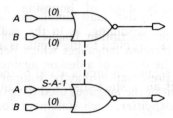

Fig. 6.7 Concurrent fault simulation.

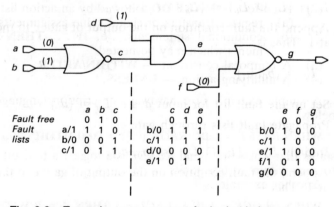

	a	b	c		c	d	e		e	f	g
Fault free		0	1	0		0	1	0		0	0	1
Fault	a/1	1	1	0	b/0	1	1	1	b/0	1	0	0
lists	b/0	0	0	1	c/1	1	1	1	c/1	1	0	0
	c/1	0	1	1	d/0	0	0	0	e/1	1	0	0
					e/1	0	1	1	f/1	0	1	0
									g/0	0	0	0

Fig. 6.8 Example on concurrent fault simulation.

As in the previous examples let the inputs be $a = f = 0$ and $b = d = 1$. Postulated faults on the first gate are $a/1$, $b/0$ and $c/1$; since $a/1$ produces the same output as the fault-free circuit it is removed from the fault list.

Postulated faults on the second gate are $b/0$, $c/1$, $d/0$ and $e/1$; $d/0$ produce the same output response as the faulty gate and is thus removed from the fault list.

Postulated faults on the last gate are $b/0$, $c/1$, $e/1$, $f/1$ and $g/0$. All of these conditions produce a response which differs from the fault-free output, consequently these fault conditions can be detected by the given input pattern.

The amount of storage required by the concurrent fault simulator is greater than that required by the deductive fault simulator since all the differences between the faulty and fault-free circuits are stored in the fault lists, whereas in deductive fault simulation only the differences in gate output states are stored. Furthermore, in concurrent fault simulation events occurring due to changes in both the faulty and fault-free circuits must be scheduled. It is considered, however, that the simulation process is faster than the deduction process.

6.6 Future trends

6.6.1 HARDWARE DESCRIPTION LANGUAGES

Hierarchical design methodologies necessitate the development of languages which enable the behaviour of a system to be described or specified at a high level of abstraction. Register transfer languages achieved this objective to some extent, but have the disadvantage of imposing a particular form of implementation.

To date, several hardware description languages have evolved, some of which are, in essence, specification languages which permit the behaviour of the system to be defined at the outset of a design, against which the behaviour of lower levels of system representation may be compared.

Although the actual format of the languges used to describe the behaviour of a system at a high level may differ, each statement comprises the following components,

(1) A cause — **WHEN**
(2) An effect — **MAKE/DO** followed by an action list which may comprise
    (a) register transfers or signal value assignments;
    (b) conditional statements, i.e. **IF . . . THEN . . . ELSE . . .** statements which may be nested.
(3) A temporal constraint — **WITHIN/AFTER**
(4) A nullifying action — **UNLESS**.

A simple example of a hardware description language statement is shown below.

WHEN $RESET$ = 1 **DO** $REGA$ (0:3) = 0000 **WITHIN** 10.

states that when the signal $RESET$ is a logic 1 a four-bit register REGA is set to zero within 10 time units.

Another example is

WHEN $CLOCK$ = 1 **IF** $SELECT$ = 1 **THEN** $A = B$ **WITHIN** 5
                  ELSE $A = C$ **WITHIN** 5.

Stating that when the $CLOCK$ is a logic 1, if $SELECT$ is also a logic 1, A is set to B within 5 time units; however, if $SELECT$ is not a logic 1, then A is set to C within 5 time units.

Several examples of these functional/hardware description languages are FDL [24], STRICT [25], HILO [26] and ELLA. [27]

6.6.2 DEDUCTIVE FAULT SIMULATION AT HIGHER LEVELS OF ABSTRACTION [28]

Most fault simulators work at gate level; however, this is very inefficient when used on large circuits. In order to improve the efficiency of this process the concepts underlying the technique of deductive fault simulation have been applied to systems whose behaviour has been described in terms of a hardware/specification language. Deductive fault simulation, however, cannot be applied directly to the high-level description of the system which must be transformed into a set of Boolean equations; these are then used to propagate fault conditions as at gate level.

The essence of the transformation of the high-level description into a set of Boolean equations is to assign a control variable to each conditional statement in a given section of the description and thereafter express the outcome of an action in a form which includes the effect of the control variables. For example, consider the conditional statement

$$\textbf{IF } a. \text{ AND. } b \quad \textbf{THEN } y1 = AND \ (c,d,e)$$
$$\textbf{ELSE } y2 = OR \ (f,g)$$

The transformation is obtained as follows.

First, assign a control variable $C1$ to the conditional part of the statement, i.e. $C1 = ab$.

Second, express the assignments to $y1$ and $y2$ in terms of $C1$, i.e.

$$y1 = (c.d.e). \ \underline{C1}$$
$$y2 = (f + g). \ \overline{C1}$$

The technique of deductive fault simulation can then be applied to the Boolean expressions.

Although this technique is conceptually straightforward, in practice it can be extremely difficult to perform the transformation, particularly if the description contains conditional statements with many levels of nesting, and also when the actions, themselves, are functions other than simple assignments or logical operations, for example, arithmetic or bit manipulation functions.

6.6.3 VERIFICATION AND SYMBOLIC SIMULATION [29, 30]

Hardware/specification languages, in addition to providing a high-level template of a system, have been developed for another reason. It has long been recognized that simulation, as a vehicle for verifying a design, is an incomplete process, since, when simulation is used as a verification tool the only valid conclusion which can be deduced from the results is that the design will produce the correct outputs for the small set of test inputs which have been applied. Consequently, in an attempt to verify a design completely or at least be able to define the level of verification obtained, researchers have been applying techniques, similar to those used for 'program proving', to high-level descriptions of digital systems in an attempt to verify a design without using simulation.

Another technique which has been developed for design verification is symbolic simulation. This technique has evolved from the symbolic execution of computer programs where symbols are used for the values of program variables.

To illustrate the basic concept of symbolic simulation of a hardware function, consider three four-bit registers *REGA*, *REGB* and *REGC*, and assume that *REGC* will contain the result of OR-ing the contents of *REGA* and *REGB*. That is,

REGC = *REGA* .OR. *REGB*

Let the contents of *REGA* = 1001 (symbolically $REGA).
Let the contents of *REGB* = 001 (symbolically $REGB).
In the normal simulator after some delay

REGC = 1011

However, symbolically,

REGC = $REGA. OR. $REGB

In the normal simulation, further operations on *REGC* would only involve the contents of *REGC*, i.e. 1011; however, in symbolic simulation we are left with the actual operations and if *REGC* is involved with another function, the function operates on $REGA. OR. $REGB, so that this symbolic value expands as it is combined with other symbolic values. This situation is further complicated when conditional clauses in a system description are evaluated, since all branches must be processed; this is in contrast to a specific test case when one branch or another is followed depending upon the specific value of the test case. It is considered that, although symbolic simulation must process all branches in a conditional statement, it is far more efficient and reliable than if all possible test cases were run individually.

6.6.4 ALTERNATIVE TO SOFTWARE SIMULATION [31–3]

The growing complexity of VLSI circuits demands an increase in the efficiency of CAD tools. This efficiency is currently limited by the use of computers which have a general purpose architecture as the host machine for the CAD tool. In order to overcome this efficiency barrier special purpose computers have been developed which exploit the parallelism or concurrency that exists in the algorithms implemented in the CAD tool.

In a gate level simulator, the ability to simultaneously evaluate all gate changes occurring at a given instant would greatly enhance simulation efficiency. At present, the evaluation of concurrent events is achieved by freezing time and thereafter evaluating each gate change individually; that is, if twenty gates had an input change, then the evaluation time would be twenty times that of a single gate. Consequently, a salient feature of all hardware simulators designed to date is a high degree of parallelism in the hardware which performs the gate evaluation function; for example, the Yorktown Simulation Engine [32], which can perform two billion gate evaluations per second, comprises many logic processors, each of which can simulate 4096 arbitrary four-input functions, and array processors for simulating RAMs and ROMs. The Logic Simulation Machine is another example of a hardware simulator which employs many parallel evaluation modules. It may be considered that a large number of parallel evaluation modules would be required when simulating a large circuit; however, if the concept of selective trace simulation is implemented in the machine the number of parallel modules required can be kept to an acceptable number. Within the logic simulation machine [33], further increases in simulation efficiency are obtained by using a cache memory in conjunction with a 'data lookahead' technique to exploit the advantages of event-driven simulation. Since it is known in advance which sections of the circuit will be evaluated next, the data relevant to these sections is read into the cache memory, whilst the simulator is evaluating gate changes, ready to be passed to the evaluation modules when required. The efficiency of the event scheduling process may also be improved by implementing it as a hardware priority queue in such a way that the processing time of the queue is independent of its length.

Although hardware simulators offer a speed advantage of at least twenty times that of a software simulator, it is considered that their use is an interim solution to the problem of verifying VLSI circuits and will superseded by more formal methods of verification as currently used in computer science for program proving. [34]

References

1. Kao, W.H., Faith, N., Madden, J.A. and Wen, C.C. ISIS: an integrated simulation system for process-device-circuit design, *Proc. International Conference on Computer Aided Design*, 147–50 (1983).
2. McCalla, W.J. and Pederson, D.O. Elements of computer aided circuit analysis. *IEEE Trans. Circuit Theory*, **CT-8**(1), 14–26 (1971).
3. Vladimerscu, A., Newton, A.R. and Pederson, D.O. *SPICE: Version 2F.1 User's Guide*. Department of Electrical Engineering and Computer Sciences, University of California, Berkeley (1972).
4. Ruehli, A.E. and Dilton, G.S. Circuit analysis, logic simulation and design verification for VLSI. *Proc. IEEE*, **71**(1), 34–47 (1983).
5. Hachtel, G.D. *et al*. The sparse tableau approach to network analysis and design. *IEEE Trans. Circuit Theory*, **CT-18**, 101–8 (1971).
6. Newton, A.R. Techniques for the simulation of large scale integrated circuits. *IEEE Trans. Circuits and Systems*, **CAS-26**(9), 741–9 (1979).
7. Arnout, G. and De Man, H.J. The use of threshold functions and Boolean controlled network elements for macromodeling of LSI circuits. *IEEE J. Solid State Circuits*, **SC-23**(3), 326–32 (1978).
8. Chawla, B.R., Gummel, H.K. and Kosak, P. Motis — an MOS timing simulator. *IEEE Trans. Circuits and Systems*, **CAS-22**(12), 901–10 (1975).
9. Bryant, R.E. Mossim: a switch level simulator for MOS LSI. *18th Design Automation Conference Proceedings*, 786–90 (1981).
10. Russell, G. GAELIC logic simulator: an interactive CAD tool. *Computer Aided Design*, **12**(4), 195–8 (1980).
11. Syzgenda, S.A. and Thompson, E.W. Digital logic simulation in a time-based, table driven environment: Part I design verification. *Computer*, **8**, 23–36 (1975).
12. Thomas, J.J. Automated diagnostic test programs for digital networks. *Computer Design*, 63–6 (August 1971).
13. Putzola, G. and Roth, J.P. A heuristic algorithm for the testing of asynchronous circuits. *IEEE Trans. Computers*, **C-20**(6), 639–47 (1971).
14. Goel, P. and Rosales, C.B. PODEM-X: an automatic test generation system for

VLSI logic structures. *18th Design Automation Conference Proceedings*, 260–8 (1981).

15. Coelho, D.R. Behavioural simulation of LSI and VLSI circuits. *VLSI Design*, 42–51 (February 1984).

16. Des Marias, P.J. Shew, E.S.Y. and Wilcox, P.S. A functional level modelling language for digital simulation. *19th Design Automation Conference Proceedings*, 315–20 (1982).

17. Agrawal, V.D. *et al.* A mixed mode simulator. *17th Design Automation Conference Proceedings*, 618–25 (1980).

18. Stevens, P. and Arnout, G. BIMOS: An MOS Oriented Multi-level Logic Simulator. *20th Design Automation Conference Proceedings*, 100–5 (1983).

19. Eichelberger, E.B. Hazard detection in combinational and sequential switching circuits. *IBM J. Research and Development*, **9** 90–9 (1965).

20. Ulrich, R.G. Exclusive simulation of activity in digital networks. *Comm. ACM*, **12**(2), 102–110 (1969).

21. Szygenda, S.A. and Thompson, E.W. Digital logic simulation in a time-based table driven environment: Part II parallel fault simulation. *Computer*, **8**, 39–49 (1975).

22. Armstrong, D.B. A deductive method for simulating faults in large circuits. *IEEE Trans. Computers*, **C-21**(5), 469–71 (1972).

23. Ulrich, E.G. and Baker, E.T. Concurrent simulation of nearly identical digital networks. *Computer*, 39–44 (April 1974).

24. Noon, W.A. A design verification and logic validation system. *14th Design Automation Conference Proceedings*, 362–8 (1977).

25. McLauchlan, M.R. High level languages in design. Chapter 12 of this book.

26. Rappaport, A. Digital logic simulator software supports behavioural models. *EDN*, **28**(10), 95–8 (1983).

27. Morison, J.D., Peeling, N.E. and Thorp, T.L. ELLA: a hardware description language. *Proc. IEEE Intern. Conf. Circuits and Computers* (1982).

28. Premachandran, R.M. and Chappell, S.G. Deductive fault simulation with functionl blocks. *IEEE Trans. Computers*, **C-27**(8), 689–95 (1978).

29. Darringer, J.A. The application of program verification techniques to hardware verification. *16th Design Automation Conference Proceedings*, 375–81 (1979).

30. Carter, W.C., Joyner, W.H. and Brand, D. Symbolic simulation of correct machine design. *16th Design Automation Conference Proceedings*, 280–6 (1979).

31. Barto, R. and Syzgenda, S.A. A computer architecture for digital logic simulation. *Electronic Engineering*, 35–66 (1980).

32. Denneau, M.M. The Yorktown simulation engine. *19th Design Automation Conference Proceedings*, 55–9 (1982).

33. Ambrovici, M., Levendel, Y.K. and Premachandran, R.M. A logic simulation machine. *IEEE Trans. Computer Aided Design of Integrated Circuits and Systems*, **CAD-2**(2), 82–93 (1983).

34. Hantler, L.S. and King, J.C. An introduction to proving the correctness of programs. *Computing Surveys*, **8**(3), 331–53 (1976).

Appendix

Table A.1   Circuit simulation

Existing Programs:	ASPEC, ASTAP, DIANA, IMAG III, MSINC, SLIC-M, SPICE, SPLICE.
Function	To perform accurate a.c., d.c. and transient analysis, and also, noise, temperature and sensitivity analysis.
Simulation primitives	Resistors, capacitors and inductors, diodes, bipolar transistors, field-effect transistors, sub-circuits.
Signals	Currents and voltages as functions of time.
Algorithms	Non-linear analysis techniques. Numerical integration techniques. Sparse matrix techniques.
Comments	(1) Very close link to technology.
	(2) Ideally, the input to this level of simulator should come directly from the layout.
	(3) Simulation accuracy is limited only by the device model accuracy.
	(4) Major applications in digital circuitry are
	(a) simulation of circuits with tight coupling between input and output: e.g., Schmitt triggers, sense, amplifiers, flip-flops;
	(b) examination of electric faults which do not manifest themselves as logical faults: e.g., clock feed through, charge sharing.
	(5) Used extensively for the characterization of basic cells.

Table A.2   Timing simulator

Existing programs:	DIANA, MOTIS, SPLICE.
Function	Time domain analysis of digital circuits.
Simulation primitives	Basic logic functions represented internally by macromodels or connections of transistors which are individually modelled using device look-up tables.
Signals	Time domain waveforms.
Algorithms	Similar to those at circuit level simulation coupled with selective trace.
Comments	(1) Due to the use of simplified transistor models simulation time is greatly reduced in comparison to circuit simulation.
	(2) Slightly less accurate than circuit simulation.
	(3) Electrical loading and bidirectional devices can be simulated.
	(4) Can be used economically on circuits with several thousand devices.
	(5) Close link to technology still maintained.

Table A.3   Switch level simulation

Existing programs	MOSSIM
Function	Function verification of a circuit as realized on the layout.
Simulation primitives	FET switches — Network is considered as nodes connected by transistors.
Signals	Three-valued logic.
Algorithms	'Dynamic topology' algorithm.
Comments	(1) Simulation model is based on the actual layout structure and not upon the intended function. (2) Due to the simplified models the circuit can be extracted directly from the layout. (3) In comparison to circuit level models, the circuit is represented in an idealized way. (4) Has the advantage over gate level simulation in that it can readily model the bidirectional characteristics of pass-transistors. (5) Can provide an improved model for simulating short circuits in MOS gate structures.

Table A.4   Gate level

Existing programs	DECSIM, DIGSIM, FLOGIC, GAELIC, LAMP, SALOGS, TEGAS.
Function	To perform logic and design verification, spike and hazard analysis and fault simulation.
Simulation primitives	AND, NAND, OR and NOR gates, flip flops, shift registers, etc.
Signals	Discrete logic values.
Algorithms	Synchronous-asynchronous next event. Selective trace.
Comments	(1) Capable of simulating systems comprising 20 000 AEGs (active element groups). (2) Exploits the unilateral switching characteristics of logic gates. (3) Approximately 1000 times faster than circuit level simulation. (4) Tenuous link with technology.
Disadvantages	(1) Does not allow for adequate representation of some typical LSI and VLSI design problems, e.g. clock breakthrough. (2) Does not allow ready modelling of components with bidirectional switching characteristics.

Table A.5   Behavioural level

Existing programs	LAMP, FLOGIC, SABLE, TEGAS.
Function	Design verification.
Simulation primitives	(1) Built-in functions ranging from simple gates to more complex functions, e.g. decoders, counters, ALUs, etc. (2) Functional modelling language description of primitives. (3) User-defined functions described by a sub-set of some programming language.
Signals	Logic 1s and logic 0s, octal, decimal and hexadecimal numbers.
Algorithms	Asynchronous next-event. Selective trace.
Comments	(1) This level of simulation was introduced to maintain the continuum of simulation resolution existing from circuit through to gate level but absent from gate to register transfer level. (2) Specification of a logic function by means of a modelling language eliminates the necessity of updating a function library, furthermore a single interpretive program can simulate all functions.

Table A.6   Mixed mode simulation

Existing programs	DIANA, SPLICE.
Function	Design verification.
Simulation primitives	Logic elements, timing elements, circuit elements.
Signals	Logic levels and voltages as a function of time.
Algorithms	Dependent upon the level of simulation.
Comments	(1) Permits different levels of simulation to be performed simultaneously, e.g. in simulating a RAM the decoder may be simulated at gate level, the sense amplifiers at circuit level and the output buffers at timing level. (2) Nodes in the circuit must be labelled as either logic, timing or circuit. (3) Whenever a signal crosses an interface between sections of the circuit described at a different level the signal must undergo logic to voltage conversion and vice versa.

7 Automatic test pattern generation

7.1 Introduction

In addition to the problems of verifying complex circuit designs prior to fabrication, a second major issue in the design of VLSI circuits is that of isolating faulty devices immediately after fabrication. The devices suffer from a wide range of defects which occur in the fabrication process [1]; for example, pin holes in the gate oxide, shorted or open interconnect lines (polysilicon, diffusion or metal), contact hole defects, contaminations, crystalline defects on the wafer. There are also design faults, such as a gate output having insufficient drive capability for its output capacitance.

To isolate these faulty devices, it is necessary to apply a set of input waveforms which will result in a different response from the faulty and fault-free circuits. In the past, these input waveforms were generated manually; however, as circuit complexities increased manual methods were partially replaced by automatic test generation methods. With present day circuit complexities the cost of test generation is extremely high and grows almost exponentially with circuit size. In an attempt to curtail this growth rate various design methodologies have evolved to enhance the testability of circuits and so maintain test generation costs at an acceptable level. The techniques for designing testable circuits will be discussed in Chapter 8.

7.2 Test generation methods

Test generation methods are divided into two classes, namely those which use the logic equations to generate the tests and are referred to as the algebraic or functional methods and those which use topological gate level descriptions for test generation, referred to as the structural methods.

Historically, test generation methods have been directed at generating tests to detect the 'classical' faults, that is those which manifest themselves as a gate output stuck-at-1 (s-a-1) or stuck-at-0 (s-a-0). The ability to generate tests only for those faults which can be modelled as a gate output stuck at some logic value excludes the testing of a large number of possible faults, called 'non-classical' faults, which occur in present-day integrated circuits. Some examples of non-classical faults are shorted or open interconnections which change the logical function of the circuit: for example, a short circuit between two signal lines may introduce an asynchronous feedback loop into a section of combinational circuitry, or in the case of CMOS circuits [2] a simple NOR gate in the presence of a stuck-at-open fault is transformed into a logic function which has a 'memory'. In recent years, with the changes in technology the number of failure modes manifesting themselves as non-classical faults has increased; the validity of only testing circuits for the presence of classical faults has been questioned and found not to be wholly satisfactory, so that the modelling of non-classical fault conditions for the purposes of test generation has become an active research topic.

7.2.1 COMBINATIONAL TEST GENERATION METHODS

Although there are many techniques for generating tests in combinational circuits only the Boolean difference method and path sensitization techniques will be discussed as illustrative examples of an algebraic and a structural method of test pattern generation.

Boolean difference method [3]

Consider an arbitrary combinational circuit realizing some function $F(X)$, where X represents a number of Boolean input variables $(x_1, x_2, x_3, \ldots, x_n)$. In order to detect a fault in this function, the complement of $F(X)$ must be generated when one of the input variables x_i is negated. That is,

$$F(x_1, x_2, \ldots, 1, \ldots, x_n) \oplus F(x_1 x_2, \ldots, 0, \ldots, x_n) = 1$$

The left-hand side of the above equation is called the Boolean difference and is represented by the derivative operator d/dx_i. The Boolean difference thus defines all conditions in which the output of the function is dependent solely upon the condition of x_i. Thus a test for a fault condition on x_i exists if $dF(X)/dx_i = 1$; however, if $dF(X)/dx_i = 0$, then x_i has no effect on the function, and hence a test for a fault condition on x_i does not exist.

The set of tests which would detect a fault on x_i is obtained by performing the logical AND operation between the Boolean difference and the logic value opposite to the fault condition on x_i, that is, if x_i is stuck-at-1 (s-a-1) then the set of all tests T for this fault condition is derived from $\bar{x}_i.dF(X)/dx_i$, and if x_i is stuck-at-0 (s-a-0), $T = x_i.dF(X)/dx_i$.

The above technique can be extended readily to generated test for faults on internal nodes in the circuit. In this instance, the output of the faulty gate is considered to be a pseudo input h to the circuit, and the Boolean function of the circuit is derived in terms of the original inputs and the pseudo input h. Then the Boolean difference equation with respect to h is formulated:

$$dF(X,h)/dh = F(x_1, x_2, \ldots x_n, h) \oplus F(x_1, x_2, \ldots, x_n, \bar{h})$$

The set of tests to detect a fault on h is derived from the following Boolean expressions.

If h is stuck-at-0,

$$T = h(x_1, x_2, \ldots, x_n).dF\ (X,\ h)/dh$$

where $h(x_1, x_2, \ldots, x_n)$ defines the necessary input conditions to make node h a logic 1.

If h is stuck-at-1 (s-a-1)

$$T = \hbar\ (x_1, x_2, \ldots, x_n).dF(X,h)/dh$$

where $\hbar\ (x_1, x_2, \ldots, x_n)$ defines necessary input conditions to make node h a logic 0.

Example Consider the circuit shown in Fig. 7.1, in which the fault condition line h s-a-0 exists, i.e. the output of gate 6 is s-a-0. The first step in generating a test for this fault condition is to derive the Boolean expression for the output of the circuit in terms of the primary inputs and line h which is assumed to be disconnected, temporarily, from gate 6 and considered as a pseudo input.

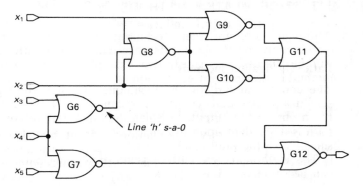

Fig. 7.1 Example circuit.

Let the output function be $F(X,h)$, where $X = (x_1, x_2, x_3, x_4, x_5)$.

$$F(X,h) = \overline{G11 + G7} = \overline{G11} \cdot \overline{G7}$$

$$= \overline{(G9 + G10)} \cdot \overline{G7}$$

$$= \overline{((x_1 + G8) + (x_2 + G8))} \cdot \overline{G7}$$

$$= (x_1 x_2 + G8) \cdot \overline{G7} = (x_1 x_2 + G8)(x_4 + x_5)$$

$$= (x_1 x_2 + \overline{h}\ \overline{x_1}\ \overline{x_2})(x_4 + x_5)$$

$$dF(X,h)/dh = F(X,h=0) \oplus F(X,h=1)$$

$$F(X,h=0) = (x_1 x_2 + \overline{x_1}\ \overline{x_2})(x_4 + x_5)$$

$$F(X,h=1) = x_1 x_2 (x_4 + x_5)$$

Hence $dF(X,h)/dh = \overline{x}_1\ \overline{x}_2\ (x_4 + x_5)$

Expressing the logic function at the output of gate 6 in terms of the primary input,

$h(x_1, x_2, x_3, x_4, x_5) = \overline{x_3 + x_4}$

The set of all tests to detect the fault condition is given by

$$T = h(X)\ dF(X,h)/dh$$

$$= \overline{(x_3 + x_4)}\ (\overline{x}_1\ \overline{x}_2)\ (x_4 + x_5)$$

$$= \overline{x}_1\ \overline{x}_2\ \overline{x}_3\ \overline{x}_4\ x_5$$

i.e. the fault on gate 6 will be detected by setting $x_1 = x_2 = x_3 = x_4 = 0$ and $x_5 = 1$.

Path sensitization methods

The concept underlying the technique of test pattern generation using path sensitization methods comprises tracing a signal path from the site of the fault to an observable output, in which the logic state at any gate output along the path is dependent upon the logic value at the site of the fault, i.e. the path is sensitive to the fault condition.

The method of test pattern generation using path sensitization techniques can be summarized as follows:

(1)   At the site of the fault, specify the inputs to the faulty gate to make its output response sensitive to the fault condition.

(2)   Sensitize a path, from the site of the fault to an observable output, by assigning non-dominant logic values to each input of a gate, except the input propagating the fault condition, so that the output of that gate is sensitive to the fault condition. In this way the effect of the fault is propagated to an observable output. This propagation of fault information is the essence of structural methods for test pattern generation.

(3)   By the process of backward simulation, determine the set of primary input values necessary to make the gate at the site of the fault sensitive to the fault condition and also to sensitize the path to an observable output. The set input values so derived constitute the test for the fault condition. As an example of the technique consider the circuit shown in Fig. 7.2, where it is considered that the output of gate 1 is stuck-at-0.

Method

(1)   Make the output of gate 1 sensitive to the fault condition by assigning a logic 1 to both inputs, so that in the fault-free circuit the output would be a logic 1, i.e. opposite to that of the fault condition.

(2)   Propagate information about the fault condition through gate 3 to an observable point by assigning a logic 0 to the second input to gate 3. In

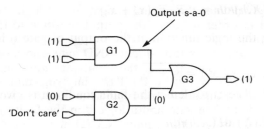

Fig. 7.2 Example on path sensitization.

this way the logic value on the output of gate 3 depends upon the presence or absence of the fault on gate 1.

(3) By a process of backward simulation justify the logic assignments made in making the faulty gate sensitive to the fault condition and also propagating it to an observable output. This process starts from the observable gate output and regresses to the primary inputs to the circuit. Thus the assignment of logic 0 to the output of gate 2 must be justified by assigning a logic 0 to either of the inputs to gate 2. Since no other logic values require justification the test for the fault condition comprises the assignment of a logic 1 to both inputs to gate 1 and a logic 0 assignment to either input of gate 2. The output of gate 3 under fault-free conditions is a logic 1, whilst if the fault is present it is a logic 0.

The path sensitization method described above sensitizes only a single path from the site of the fault to an observable output and fails to generate a test for a fault in a circuit containing a reconvergent fanout structure. This weakness in the method is overcome in the D-algorithm, described below, which sensitizes all paths from the site of a fault to an observable output.

D-*algorithm* [4]

The *D*-algorithm is a more formal specification of the path sensitization method, described above, in which a symbol D is assigned to the fault-sensitive nodes in the circuit, permitting all possible sensitized paths to be readily identified, and systematically processed until a path is traced to an observable output.

The *D*-algorithm is based on the 'Calculus of *D*-cubes'; therefore, before describing the processes within the *D*-algorithm some of its associated terminology will be explained.

(1) *D-cube.* The mapping of the minterms of a Boolean function onto a Karnaugh map is well known; alternatively, the minterms may be mapped onto the vertices of a *n*-dimensional cube. Each vertex is identified by an ordered *n*-tuple comprising the inputs or variables in the Boolean function, which normally have the values 0, 1 and *X* (don't care). In the context of the *D*-algorithm, a variable may also assume the fault-sensitive value *D*, hence the *n*-tuple associated with some vertex is referred to as a *D*-cube.

(2) *Primitive* D-*cube of failure (PDCF).* The primitive *D*-cube of failure

simply defines the miniml assignment of logic values to the inputs of a gate in order to make the output sensitive to the fault condition. For example:

(a) Consider a three-input AND gate whose output is stuck-at-0 (s-a-0). Assuming that the inputs are a,b,c and the output is d, the PDCF would be $1^a1^b1^cD^d$, implying that a logic 1 is assigned to each input a,b and c, and the output d would be a logic 1 in the fault-free gate and a logic 0 in the faulty gate.

(b) Consider a three-input NAND in which the output is stuck-at-1 (s-a-1), again assuming the inputs are a,b,c and output d. The PDCF would be $1^a1^b1^c\bar{D}^d$, implying that each input is assigned a logic 1 and the output of the fault-free gate is a logic 0 and the faulty gate a logic 1.

If the output of the NAND gate was stuck-at-0, then three PDCFs would exist, namely $0^aX^bX^cD^d$, $X^a0^bX^cD^d$ and $X^aX^b0^cD^d$, where X denotes a don't care value.

The simple rule to generate a PDCF for a fault on a gate input is to assign to the faulty input the logic value opposite to the fault condition and to all other inputs the non-dominant logic value for that particular type of gate. The output of the gate is then assigned a D or $\bar{D}$ depending upon whether the fault-free response for the assignments is a logic 1 or a logic 0 respectively.

(3) *Propagation D-cube (PDC)*. The propagation D-cube defines the assignment of logic values to the inputs to a gate, other than those propagating fault information, in order to make the output of the gate sensitive to the incoming fault information. It should be noted that more than one input may be propagating this information (e.g. in a circuit with a reconvergent fanout); in this case the PDC is referred to as a multiple propagation D-cube. In a multiple propagation D-cube, if both a D *and* $\bar{D}$ occur on the inputs the output of the gate will assume a fixed logic value inhibiting the propagation of fault information beyond this gate. Table 7.1 illustrates the propagation D-cubes for the four

Table 7.1 Single propagation D-cubes for the four standard logic functions. It is assumed that each gate has three inputs a, b, c and an output d.

NAND gate					*AND gate*			
a	b	c	d		a	b	c	d
D	1	1	$\bar{D}$		D	1	1	D
1	D	1	$\bar{D}$		1	D	1	D
1	1	D	$\bar{D}$		1	1	D	D

NOR gate					*OR gate*			
a	b	c	d		a	b	c	d
D	0	0	$\bar{D}$		D	0	0	D
0	D	0	$\bar{D}$		0	D	0	D
0	0	D	$\bar{D}$		0	0	D	D

standard logic functions. It should be noted that the Ds and $\bar{D}s$ in the propagation D-cubes may be interchanged, since the PDC simply defines the conditions to be satisfied to propagate the fault information and indicate whether or not the fault information is inverted in the process. However, at the outset of the D-algorithm process once the significance of the D and $\bar{D}$ has been defined, the definition must not be altered until the process is complete.

(4) *Primitive cube (PC)*. The primitive cube simply defines the minimal assignment of logic values to the inputs of a gate in order to achieve some defined output value. Table 7.2 illustrates the primitive cubes for the four standard logic functions.

Table 7.2 Primitive cubes for the four standard logic functions. It is assumed that each gate has three inputs a, b, c and output d.

NAND gate				AND gate			
a	b	c	d	a	b	c	d
0	X	X	1	0	X	X	0
X	0	X	1	X	0	X	0
X	X	0	1	X	X	0	0
1	1	1	0	1	1	1	1

NOR gate				OR gate			
a	b	c	d	a	b	c	d
1	X	X	0	1	X	X	1
X	1	X	0	X	1	X	1
X	X	1	0	X	X	1	1
0	0	0	1	0	0	0	0

(5) *D-intersection process*. The D-intersection process is a means of simultaneously matching the logic assignments which already exist in a circuit as a result of the D-algorithm up to a particular point with those required to propagate the fault condition through a successor gate. The D-intersection rules are shown in Table 7.3.

The basic steps in the D-algorithm method of test pattern generation are outlined below.

(1) Select a fault.
(2) Generate the primitive D-cube of failure.
(3) Sensitize at least one path from the site of the fault to an observable output node. This path sensitization procedure is referred to as the D-drive process. The D-drive process starts at the output of the faulty gate; the effect of the fault is then propagated through all the gates in the fanout list of the faulty gate, by performing a D-intersection initially between the PDCF of the faulty gate and the propagation D-cube of the first gate in the fanout list of the faulty gate. The results of the

Table 7.3   *D*-intersection rules

∩	0	1	X	D	$\bar{D}$
0	0	∅	0	Ψ	Ψ
1	∅	1	1	Ψ	Ψ
X	0	1	X	D	$\bar{D}$
D	Ψ	Ψ	D	μ	λ
$\bar{D}$	Ψ	Ψ	$\bar{D}$	λ	μ

∅   Empty intersection resulting from inconsistent assignment of logic values to a node in the circuit.

Ψ   Undefined intersection in which an attempt has been made to match a fault-sensitive value with a fixed logic value.

μ   Permissible intersection between fault sensitive values i.e. $D \cap D = D$ or $\bar{D} \cap \bar{D} = \bar{D}$.

λ   Attempt to intersect fault-sensitive values of different polarity. This inconsistency can be resolved, usually, if in the propagation *D*-cube all occurrences of D and $\bar{D}$ are changed to $\bar{D}$ and D respectively. However, if during a given intersection process a μ-intersection has already occurred, interchanging Ds and $\bar{D}$s will not resolve the conflict.

intersection process are then stored in the 'test-cube' of the circuit for this stage of the process. This test-cube is then *D*-intersected with the propagation *D*-cube of the next gate in the fanout list of the faulty gate forming another test-cube, which is then *D*-intersected with the propagation *D*-cube of another gate in the fanout list of the faulty gate. This process is repeated until all gates in the fanout list of the faulty gate have been processed. Thereafter, for each gate through which the fault information has been propagated, an attempt is made to propagate this information through the gates in their fanout lists. This procedure is continued until an observable output is reached.

(3)   The final stage in the *D*-algorithm is the *consistency operation* where, by means of a backward simulation technique, the assignments of logic ones and zeros used in the formation of the primitive *D*-cube of failure and the propagation *D*-cubes are justified. The consistency operation starts at the inputs to the gate where the *D*-drive process terminated, because the output of this gate was observable, and regresses to the primary inputs. The assignment of logic ones and zeros to the primary inputs is the test for the fault condition.

Example   As an example of the *D*-algorithm method of test pattern generation, consider the circuit, shown in Fig. 7.1, in which the output of gate 6 is s-a-0. See Table 7.4.

7.2.2 SEQUENTIAL TEST GENERATION METHODS

Although adequate test generation methods exist for detecting faults in combinational circuits, the same cannot be said for sequential circuits. The major difficulty is that the output response of a sequential circuit depends not only on the present input values but also on the stored states in the circuit. Therefore in order to detect a fault in a sequential circuit a series of test vectors must be applied, rather than a single test vector as in the combinational circuit.

Due to the problems of testing sequential circuits, several design techniques have been devised which permit sequential circuits to be reconfigured in such a way that, for the purposes of testing, the circuit is essentially combinational; these design techniques will be discussed in Chapter 8. Although there is a tendency, at present, to modify sequential circuits for the purposes of testing and test pattern generation, some of the techniques for sequential test pattern generation are worthy of a brief discussion.

Iterative test generation method [5]

In this technique a sequential circuit is converted into an iterative combinational circuit by opening all the feedback lines, as shown in Fig. 7.3. The single fault which was assumed to exist in the sequential circuit is now considered as a multiple fault in the iterative circuit. A test T' is then generated using the D-algorithm for the multiple fault in the iterative circuit. Thereafter, by a process called 'completion' the test T' is converted into a test T for the single fault condition in the sequential circuit which differs, as shown in Fig. 7.4, from the original circuit by the insertion of a delay in the feedback line. The duration of this delay is equal to the time delay between the individual test patterns in the test sequence applied to the iterative circuit. The test T generated by the 'completion' process is then applied to a fault simulator to determine if the fault condition can in fact be detected by the sequence.

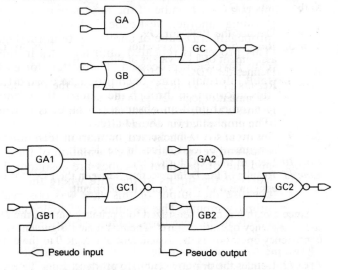

Fig. 7.3 Iterative circuit.

97 / Automatic test pattern generation

Table 7.4

	x_1	x_2	x_3	x_4	x_5	$G6$	$G7$	$G8$	$G9$	$G10$	$G11$	$G12$
(1)			0	0		D						
(2)	0	0				D		$\bar{D}$				
(3)	0	0	0	0		D		$\bar{D}$				
(4)	0							$\bar{D}$	D			
(5)	0	0	0	0		D		$\bar{D}$	D			
(6)		0						$\bar{D}$		D		
(7)	0	0	0	0		D		$\bar{D}$	D	D		
(8)									D	D	D	
(9)	0	0	0	0		D		$\bar{D}$	D	D	D	
(10)							0				D	$\bar{D}$
(11)	0	0	0	0		D	0	$\bar{D}$	D	D	D	$\bar{D}$
(12)			X	1			0					
(13)	0	0	0	0	1	D	0	$\bar{D}$	D	D	D	$\bar{D}$

Comments on Table 7.4

Line 1 Defines the primitive D-cube of failure for the fault condition, i.e. x_3 and x_4 are set to a logic 0, under fault free conditions the output of $G6$ would be a logic 1, hence it is assigned the value D.

Line 2 Defines the propagation D-cube for $G8$. Inputs x_1 and x_2 are assigned non-dominant logic values, so that the output is sensitive to the fault information propagating from $G6$. Since $G8$ is a NOR gate, the output is inverted hence the assignment of $\bar{D}$ to the output.

Line 3 Results of the D-intersection between the primitive D-cube of failure and the propagation D-cube (PDC) for $G8$. The D-intersection essentially propagates the fault information to the output of $G8$ and also ensures that the assignment of logic values to the gate inputs, so far, is consistent.

In the D-algorithm the fault information is propagated along all possible paths simultaneously. Lines 4–7 propagate the fault information from $G8$ through $G9$ and $G10$ to the inputs of $G11$.

Line 4 Defines the PDC for $G9$.

Line 5 Results of the D-intersection between the PDC for $G9$ and the current assignment of logic values in the circuit.

Line 6 Defines the PDC for $G10$.

Line 7 Results of the D-intersection between the PDC for $G10$ and the current assignment of logic values in the circuit.

Line 8 Defines a Multiple-Propagation D-cube for $G11$, since the fault information is being propagated via $G9$ and $G10$.

Line 9 Results of the D-intersection between the PDC for $G11$ and the current assignment of logic values in the circuit.

Line 10 Defines the PDC for $G12$.

Line 11 Results of the D-intersection between the PDC for $G12$ and the current assignment of logic values in the circuit.

Since a path has been sensitized to a primary output, the D-drive process stops and the consistency operation starts. The first logic assignment to be justified by the consistency operation is the assignment of a logic 0 to the output of $G7$.

Line 12 Defines the primitive cube, to produce a logic 0 on the output of $G7$; in this instance x_5 is assigned a logic 1 and x_4 a 'don't care' value which avoids an inconsistent assignment of logic values since x_4 has been assigned a logic 0.

Line 13 Results of the intersection between the primitive cube for $G7$ and the current assignment of logic values in the circuit.

In this instance all the logic assignments to internal nodes in the circuit have been justified and the consistency operation stops. The assignment of logic values to the primary inputs is the test for the fault condition, i.e. $x_1 = x_2 = x_3 = x_4 = 0$ and $x_5 = 1$; the output of the circuit has the value $\bar{D}$ indicating that the output of $G12$ would be a logic 0 if fault-free and logic 1 in the presence of a fault.

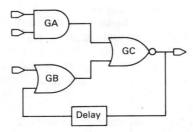

Fig. 7.4 Reconstructed circuit with delay.

Macro test generation method [5, 6]

If a circuit is highly sequential, for example, a shift register or a counter, the iterative test generation procedure does not produce acceptable tests, since the delays which have been introduced into the model used for test generation purposes produce large differences in operation between the model and the actual circuit.

In the macro test generation technique flip flops are considered as macro blocks or logical primitives in the same way as one considers NAND or NOR gates, and only feedback lines external to the macro blocks are broken when deriving an iterative circuit. The D-algorithm is then used to generate tests as before, with some modifications to perform the D-drive and consistency operation on the macro blocks.

7.3   VLSI test generation systems

The continual growth in complexity of VLSI circuits has necessitated the development of more efficient test generation tools. To date much of the published work in this area has originated from IBM in particular on the test generation procedures called PODEM-X (Path Orientated DEcision Making algorithm) and SOFTG (Simulator Orientated Fault Test Generator). The salient features of these test systems are described below.

7.3.1   PODEM-X [7]

PODEM-X is an automatic test generation system comprising three test generation programs, a fault simulator and a test pattern compaction program, which has been incorporated into IBM's design for testability methodology called LSSD (Level-Sensitive Scan Design). It has been reported that this test generation system has been used successfully on logic modules comprising 50 000 gates.

Test generation programs

A feature of an LSSD design is that for the purposes of testing, a large circuit can be partitioned into smaller subcircuits, consisting entirely of combinational logic, by blocks of shift register cells which are implicit in the LSSD style of design. These shift register blocks are instrumental in applying the test inputs to the subcircuits and also in observing the output responses from the subcircuits; consequently the registers must be tested first for possible faults before testing can begin on the combinational subcircuits. This is the function of the first of the three test generation programs called SRTG (Shift Register Test Generator). The tests performed by SRTG comprise a 'flush' and a 'shift' test; however, instead of clocking blocks of 1s and 0s or a pattern 001100, which checks all combinations of initial and next states through the registers, which can be concatenated into a single serial shift register, a pattern of either 1111. . . . , 0000. . . . , 1010. . . . or 0101. . . . is loaded initially into the registers and the main system clock is pulsed once, producing a one-stage shift in the register, and the resulting pattern is then clocked or scanned out of the register; these patterns exercise each stage of the register through all possible combinations of initial and next states.

The testing strategy incorporated into PODEM-X is to generate initially a set of 'global' tests designed to detect a large number of faults, and thereafter to generate a set of 'clean-up' tests to detect faults not covered by the global tests.

The global tests are generated by a program called RAPS (RAndom Path Sensitization test generator), whose objective is to derive an input pattern which will sensitize a large number of random paths through a circuit and then use a fault simulator to determine which faults can be detected by the input pattern. The main steps in the RAPS procedure are outlined below.

(1) Initialize all circuit nodes to a 'don't care' value.
(2) Arbitrarily select a primary output and assign to it the logic value 1 or 0.
(3) Perform a backward trace from the output until a primary input is reached, assign to this input the value decided upon from the backward trace procedure and simulate. The main objective in simulating the circuit is to determine if, with the current assignment of logic values in the circuit, the primary output is set to its specified value. A secondary effect of the simulation is the assignment of defined logic values to other nodes in the circuit.
(4) If the objective of setting the primary output to its defined value is not achieved, the backward trace procedure is repeated using nodes which have not been assigned a defined logic value; this procedure will result in another primary input being assigned a logic value. The circuit is again simulated to determine if the objective has been achieved, and if not this section of the procedure is repeated until the objective is achieved.
(5) Once the objective is achieved, another unassigned primary output is

chosen and the above procedure is repeated. The process is continued until all primary outputs have defined values.

(6) If any primary inputs have not been assigned a logic value, a search is made for a gate output, internal to the circuit, whose output is assigned but has an unassigned input. This input is then assigned a non-dominant logic value for that type of gate, and the backtracing and simulation procedures are repeated until this objective is achieved. If any primary inputs are still unassigned, this part of the procedure is repeated. However, if all the internal circuit nodes have assigned values, and some primary inputs remain unassigned, then these inputs are arbitrarily assigned logic 1 and logic 0 values.

The primary input pattern so generated is then fault simulated to determine its fault coverage.

It should be noted that in the backtrace procedure no reference is made to the controllability values (Section 8.3) of the individual gate inputs; this ensures that for each iteration of the overall procedure arbitrary choices are made in the backtrace procedure, resulting in random paths being sensitized by each of the generated test patterns.

Once a set of global tests has been generated by RAPS, a procedure called PODEM (Path Oriented DEcision Making algorithm) is called to generate a set of tests for any remaining fault conditions not covered by the global test set. The essential steps in the PODEM procedure are outlined below.

(1) Perform a structural analysis on the circuit to determine the controllability indices for the nodes in the circuit and the 'distance' that each gate output is from a primary output. The controllability indices are used in the backtrace procedure and the 'distance' that a gate is from a primary output is used to determine the shortest path to primary output when propagating fault information.

(2) Set all nodes in the circuit to a 'don't care' state.

(3) Select a fault condition on a gate.

(4) Define the objective of making the output of the gate sensitive to the fault condition. Attempt to satisfy this objective by using the backtrace and simulation procedure as performed in RAPS. In this instance, however, reference is made to the controllability indices during the backtrace procedure to improve the efficiency of the test generation technique. The controllability indices indicate the ease with which a given node can be set to some logic value; thus if, say, a NAND gate has three unassigned inputs and its output value must be a logic 1, this objective is satisfied more readily if the backtrace procedure is performed starting with the input which has the best controllability index. However, if the objective is to set the output of this gate to a logic 0, requiring a logic 1 to be assigned to each input, the backtrace procedure would start on the input with the worst controllability index, since if the conditions on this input cannot be satisfied, CPU time has not been wasted on satisfying the conditions on the other inputs.

(5) Once a value has been assigned to a primary input a five-valued simulator $(0, 1, X, D$ and $\bar{D})$ is used to determine the effect of the logic assignment to the primary input. If the initial objective of making the gate output sensitive to the fault condition is achieved, then an attempt is made to propagate the fault-sensitive information to a primary

output. If the initial objective is not achieved, the backtrace and simulation procedures are repeated until it is.

(6) Propagate the fault information from the site of the fault to a primary output, using the backtrace and simulation procedures to satisfy the necessary input conditions on the gates in setting up a sensitized path to a primary output. In some situations the fault information may be propagated along multiple paths. However, instead of systematically propagating this information along all paths, as in the D-algorithm, the distance of each gate output in the multiple path from a primary output is determined, and the shortest path is pursued.

(7) Once the final objective of propagating the fault information to the primary output is achieved, the set of logic values assigned to the primary inputs is the test for the fault condition. The input pattern is then applied to a fault simulator to determine what other faults may be detected by the test pattern.

On occasions the assignment of logic values to the primary inputs may produce conflicting logic assignments to internal nodes in the circuit. When this situation occurs the 'PI-remake' procedure is called in attempt to resolve the conflict, if possible. In this process the values of previously assigned primary inputs are successively complemented in an attempt to resolve the conflict. This process can be very time consuming and the PI-remake procedure is repeated only a limited number of times, usually equal to the number of inputs to the circuit.

Fault simulator

The fault simulator used in PODEM-X is called FFSIM (Fast Fault SIMulator) and is used to determine the faults detected by the RAPS and PODEM procedures. Since the simulator is used in an LSSD environment it need only have the capability of simulating combinational circuits.

Compaction program

Test pattern compaction programs are incorporated into PODEM-X to reduce the number of individual test patterns required to test a system by merging as many test patterns into a single test vector as possible. The compaction process can be performed either statically or dynamically.

In static compaction, the merging process is performed after the test generation phase has been completed. Extensive use is made of any unassigned primary inputs in a given set of test patterns, since tests can be merged only if the assigned values in both sets of test patterns match or if a given input in one test pattern is assigned whilst the same input in another test pattern is unassigned.

In dynamic compaction, tests are merged during the test generation phase. Initially a test for a given fault is generated, and in general not all the primary inputs are assigned logic values. Another fault is then chosen and an attempt to generate a test for this fault is made using the currently assigned primary inputs and some of the remaining unassigned inputs. This process is repeated until almost all the primary inputs have been assigned logic values. Thereafter a fault simulator is used to determine the fault cover of the compacted test.

SOFTG (Simulator Oriented Fault Test Generator) [8]

The objective in developing SOFTG was to provide a practical automatic test generator for complex sequential circuits, capable of generating long sequences and also of modelling sequential circuits accurately, since the available methods are inadequate. For example, an extension of the D-algorithm for sequential circuits called the iterative test generation method has two disadvantages: first, for the purpose of test generation a circuit larger in size to the original circuit must be produced; second, in the final stages of the procedure the circuit model used is not an accurate representation of the actual circuit.

SOFTG depends heavily on the use of a fault simulator to

(1) provide nodal logic values for the faulty and fault free circuits;
(2) store internal states for one pattern so that the test generator has the ability to discard a pattern if the simulation results are not suitable;
(3) determine what other faults a particular test pattern can detect.

Test sequences in SOFTG are generated incrementally, that is each pattern differs from its predecessor in only one bit, so that race conditions are avoided in the circuit. Furthermore SOFTG does not work its way systematically through a fault list, but dynamically selects the next fault condition based on the presence of test values (i.e. D or $\bar{D}$) at nodes in the circuit. In this way the length of test sequences are reduced since the end of one test is merged into the beginning of the next.

Before the test generation phase commences a structural analysis of the circuit is performed in order to determine the controllability indices for the nodes in the circuit and also to determine their distance from the output.

At the start of this test generation procedure all the primary inputs are assigned the value logic 0. The fault simulator is then invoked to determine what faults, if any, are detected by the pattern. All the primary inputs are now at a known value. A target fault is then selected and the objective (sensitizing the gate output at the site of the fault) is then defined. A backtrace procedure is performed until a primary input is reached. The primary input is then set to the specific value dictated by the backtrace procedure and the circuit is simulated. An analysis phase, on the outcome of the simulation results, is then performed to decide whether or not to proceed with this new pattern or to discard it and restore the node values in the circuit to the settings defined by the previous input pattern. A pattern is retained if it does not produce a conflict in node values or if it causes any faults to be detected; otherwise it is discarded. A check is then made to determine if the objective has been achieved, which in the first instance is that of making a gate output sensitive to the fault condition and second, propagating fault information to a primary output; if the objective is not achieved the backtrace and simulation procedures are continued. If at any time the backtrace procedure cannot reach a primary input, the target fault is flagged as undetected and the process is abandoned for this fault condition; an attempt to generate a test for this fault condition may be made later in the process if the conditions are right.

When SOFTG was compared with the iterative test generation method on a range of circuits whose complexity was of the order of 600 gates with approximately 80 feedback loops, SOFTG produced a fault coverage which was approximately 10% better than that achieved by the iterative test generation method, although the run times were somewhat longer.

References

1. Mangir, T.E. and Avizienis, A. Failure modes for VLSI and their effect on chip design. *IEEE Proc. First Intern. Conf. Circuits and Computers*, 685–8 (1980).
2. Wadsack, R.L. Fault modelling and logic simulation of CMOS and MOS integrated circuits. *Bell Systems Technical Journal*, **57**(5), 1449–88 (1978)
3. Selers, F.F., Hsiao, M.Y. and Bearnson, L.W. Analyzing errors with the Boolean difference. *IEEE Trans. Computers*, **C-17**(7), 676–83 (1968).
4. Roth, J.P. Diagnosis of automata failures: a calculus and a method. *IBM J. Research and Development*, **10**, 278–91 (1966).
5. Putzolu, G.R. and Roth, J.P. A heuristic algorithm for the testing of asynchronous circuits. *IEEE Trans. Computers*, **C-20**(6), 639–47 (1971).
6. Vaughn, G.D. CDALGO — a test generation program. *13th Design Automation Conference Proceedings*, 186–93 (1976).
7. Goel, P. and Rosales, B.C. PODEM-X: an automatic test generation system for VLSI logic structures. *18th Design Automation Conference Proceedings*, 260–8 (1981).
8. Snethen, T.J. Simulator oriented fault test generator. *14th Design Automation Conference Proceedings*, 88–93 (1977).

8 Design for testability

8.1 Introduction

Over the past decade circuit complexities, in terms of the number of gates, have increased test generation cost; however, this increase in cost arises not only from the size of the circuit but also from the way in which the circuit has been designed, that is, from the fact that emphasis has been placed during the design phase on the implementation of the function at the expense of due consideration of the way in which the circuit would ultimately be tested.

Regardless of the size of the circuit, various factors make test generation difficult. The first is the inability to initialize memory elements in the circuit into some known state; in the past much research work was directed at the problem of generating 'homing sequences' whose objective was to drive the circuit into some known state independent of its present state. The second factor is the inability to control or observe signal values on internal nodes in the circuit. Finally, the realization of logic functions using pass transistors which do not map readily onto equivalent gate models.

Recently, several design methodologies have evolved whose objective is to reduce not only the cost of test pattern generation but also of testing in general, by

(1) making internal nodes in a circuit more accessible;
(2) transforming sequential circuits into combinational circuits or decomposing complex circuits into less complex sub-functions for the purposes of testing;
(3) making the circuit self-testing;
(4) reducing the amount of test data which is needed to test the circuit.

Although design methodologies which improve the testability of a circuit are highly desirable, ultimately they incur some penalty with respect to the effect upon the designer and the performance of the circuit.

If the particular design style adopted to ease the testing problem is to be accepted by the design community it must be easy to apply and not so constraining as to inhibit the ingenuity of the designer; there must also be adequate software support for the particular design technique, that is, programs which will check a design for compliance to the design rules imposed by the design style. Furthermore, since most design for testability methods involve either additional hardware and/or routing, the physical size of the circuit increases and subsequently has an effect on the yield; the additional hardware also introduces extra signal delays into the circuit which affect the performance of the circuit. There is also a requirement for extra input/output pins, increasing the cost of packaging. In view of these penalties it must be demonstrated that a particular design style produces a marked reduction in test generation costs with respect to CPU time and personal effort.

8.2 Design for testability techniques

Designing for testability implies some modification to the circuit to enhance the process of test pattern generation and application. The techniques to enhance testability have been categorized into three main groups:

(1) *ad hoc* methods;
(2) structured approaches;
(3) built in test methods.

8.2.1 AD HOC METHODS [1]

Ad hoc methods evolved through the necessity to solve a particular testing problem, rather than trying to solve the problem of testing complex circuits in general by using some design methodology. The methods evolved are classified below.

(1) *Test point insertion*. Test points are routed into the circuit to make certain internal nodes more accessible in order to either control or observe the signal value on that node.

(2) *Pin amplification*. In general the number of pins on a package available for test purposes is minimal. The number of test pins, however, can be increased if some of the normal input/output pins are multiplexed to perform an additional function of acting as test inputs and outputs. However, the delays introduced by the multiplexers/demultiplexers will degrade the circuit response under normal operating conditions.

(3) *Blocking or degating logic*. In this technique additional gates are incorporated into the design to inhibit data flow along certain paths, thus partitioning the circuit into smaller modules for the purposes of testing. Blocking gates are two input gates, one input is the normal data line whilst the other is the controlling or blocking signal which can be controlled from a test input; during the normal operation of the circuit the control signal is held at the non-dominant logic value for the type of blocking gate, that is a logic one for AND, NAND or logic zero for OR, NOR.

(4) *Control and observation switching*. In this technique signal lines whose logic values are either easily controlled or observed are identified in the circuit and these are used in conjunction with demultiplexers/ multiplexers to improve the access to nodes, in close proximity to these

lines, whose logic values are difficult either to control or observe. Test mode control inputs to the multiplexers/demultiplexers determine whether the lines, whose signal values can be easily controlled or observed, are to be used for transmitting normal data or test data.

(5) *Test state registers*. Test state registers are serial input parallel output shift registers used to increase the number of test control signals which can be applied to the circuit at any given time. The input to the test state registers is usually demultiplexed with the normal inputs to the circuit. When the circuit is to be tested, test mode control inputs direct signals from the demultiplexer to the test state register; thereafter the test mode control inputs are switched so that the outputs of the demulitplexer, other than those connected to the test state register, propagate normal functional inputs or test patterns to the circuit.

Ad hoc methods for improving the testability of a circuit have the advantage of not imposing severe constraints on the designer but have the disadvantage that the methods cannot be automated, and consequently there is no software support for these techniques of designing for testability.

8.2.2 STRUCTURAL APPROACHES

In contrast to the *ad hoc* methods, the structured approaches to design for testability are more formal and are incorporated into a design from the outset rather than introduced as an afterthought as with the *ad hoc* methods.

The objective in developing the structured approach was to facilitate the testing of complex sequential circuits; consequently these approaches are directed at increasing the controllability and observability of the internal states of the circuit, essentially transforming the testing of a sequential circuit into the simpler task of testing a combinational circuit.

Over the past few years several structured approaches have evolved, namely level sensitive scan design [2], scan/set [3] and random access scan [4]; the first two methods have been adopted extensively in industry and will thus be discussed in more depth.

Level sensitive scan design (LSSD)

LSSD incorporates two design concepts namely level sensitivity and scan path.

The concept of a level sensitive design requires that the operation of the circuit is independent of the dynamic characteristics of the logic elements, that is, rise and fall times and propagation delays. Furthermore in a level sensitive design the next state of the circuit is independent of the order in which changes occur when a state change involves several input signals; this circuit chracteristic implicitly places a constraint on what signal changes can occur in the circuit, these constraints [2] however are usually applied to the clocking signals.

The major element in a level sensitive design is the polarity hold shift register latch (SRL) [2], which is used to implement all storage elements in the circuit. The SRL is similar to a master slave flip flop and is driven by two non-overlapping clocks which can be readily controlled from the primary inputs to the circuit.

107 / Design for testability

In addition to providing a circuit response which is independent of delays, the SRL play an important function in the testing of the circuit. When a circuit is implemented using the LSSD technique all the SRLs have the ability to be configured into a long serial shift register called a 'scan path', which permits the internal states in the circuit to be easily controlled or observed, since access to each storage element in the circuit is available via the scan path.

An SRL is shown symbolically in Fig. 8.1; input D is the normal signal input to the SRL, clocks C1 and C2 control the normal operation of the element, input SI is the scan path input to the element, clocks C2 and C3 control the movement of data through the SRL when it is used as part of the scan path. The output of the SRL, in normal and scan path modes, is usually taken from L2.

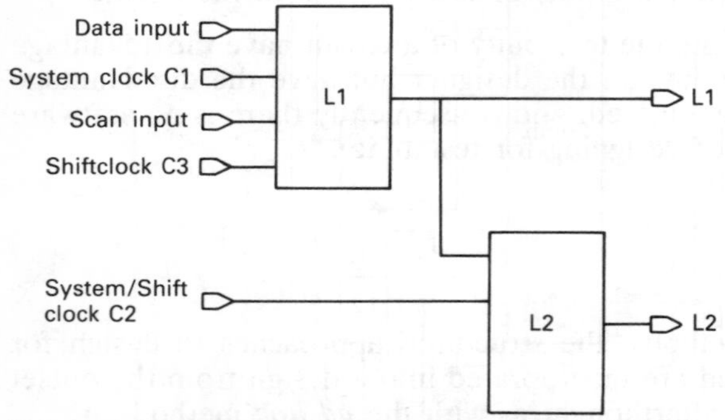

Fig. 8.1 Symbolic representation of a shift register latch.

An important feature of the LSSD design technique is that for the purposes of testing a large circuit is implicitly partitioned into smaller subcircuits, consisting entirely of combinational logic functions, by the blocks of shift register latches, as shown in Fig. 8.2, which will be instrumental in applying the test patterns to the combinational blocks and observing their response. The first phase of testing an LSSD implementation is to verify the correct operation of the latches in performing their function as a scan path by using simple 'flush' and 'shift' tests (see PODEM-X). Thereafter, the combinational subfunctions are tested in the following manner. First, the circuit is switched into test mode and the SRLs are preloaded with a test pattern which is shifted in via the scan-in port and successively stepped through each element in the scan path by pulsing clocks C3 and C2. The circuit is then switched into its normal operating mode and clock C1 is pulsed on and then off. The response of the combinational sub-functions is thus stored in the L1 latches of the SRL, and by pulsing C2 these values are duplicated in the L2 latches. The circuit is then switched back into test mode, and the contents of the L2 latches are shifted out via the scan path to the scan-out port by pulsing clocks C3 and C2. Thus by using the scan path, future states can be set up independently of the present state of the system and internal states can be easily observed, so reducing the problem of testing a sequential circuit to that of testing a combinational circuit.

The main advantages of the LSSD technique are that it removes the necessity of performing detailed timing analysis on the circuit since it is level sensitive; automatic test pattern generation is simplified since tests need only be generated for a combinational circuit; and finally since LSSD is a disciplined design methodology a design can be checked for compliance to design rules. [5]

The LSSD technique has several disadvantages, however; first the designer is constrained to implement his system as a synchronous sequential circuit; second, test times are increased since the input and output data must be scanned serially and also the system must be switched between normal and test modes; finally additional input/output pins are required for the scan-in/out ports and clocks.

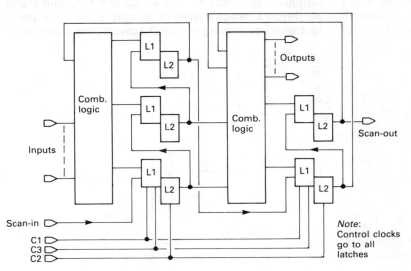

Fig. 8.2 LSSD configuration.

The particular latch configuration shown in Fig. 8.2 is called a 'double-latch' design, in which the output is taken from L2, the individual L1 and L2 latches operating in master–slave mode, guaranteeing raceless switching in the circuit. This configuration, however, has the disadvantage that two clock pulses are required before data is transferred from one partition to the next. Several modifications [6] have been made to the basic configuration of SRLs to make better use of the test hardware in the normal operation of the circuit and also to improve circuit performance. One modification consists of taking the normal system outputs from the L1 latches, the L2 latches only being used in the scan path, resulting in a configuration called the 'single latch' design. This configuration, however, requires that the circuit is partitioned into disjoint combinational blocks such that an output of an L1 latch pulsed by a C1 clock can only be used as an input to a block whose outputs are available through an L1 latch pulsed by a C2 clock and vice versa; this constraint is imposed upon the circuit to avoid races in the system. The 'single latch' operation thus has the advantage of being faster than the 'double latch' operation since only a single pulse is required before the latch outputs can be used by the system. The overhead of having a redundant L2 latch in the 'single latch' configuration, as far as normal system operation is concerned, can be removed by modifying the design of the L2 latch so that it also contains a system data input terminal, the L1 latches being controlled by C1 clocks an the modified L2 latches being controlled by the C2 clocks. In this instance the combinational logic blocks are partitioned such that the output of an L1 latch is used only as an input to a block whose output is available through a modified L2 latch, and vice versa. In this way both L1 and modified L2 latches become part of the system as well as forming the scan path for test purposes.

The basic SRL configuration has also been modified to produce a Stable Shift Register latch (SSRL) [7] by introducing a third latch L3 which is driven by the L1 latch and controlled by an independent clock P as shown in Fig. 8.3. Applications of the SSRLs comprise interfacing LSSD and non-LSSD designs, performing 'on-line' dynamic scan to assist error diagnosis in computer systems and also performing 'on-line' error detection in memories.

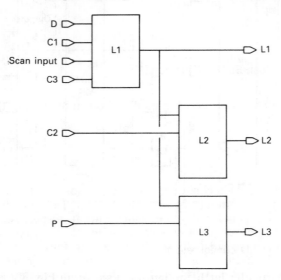

Fig. 8.3 Stable shift register latch.

Scan-set logic

In this technique, as shown in Fig. 8.4, the shift registers are not in the main data path as they are in LSSD. Furthermore, only a small number of nodes in the circuit can be monitored, the logic states of these nodes being loaded into the shift register with a single clock and thereafter shifted out via the scan-out port. Conversely in the set process N bits can be channelled into the system logic.

Since all the latches in the system may not be controlled or observed, the testing of circuits which incorporate scan/set logic is not reduced to that of testing a combinational circuit; the nodes which are to be connected to the scan/set register are usually decided upon from the results of a testability analysis program.

The scan/set register may also be used as a 'test-state' register which would permit control signals to be applied to 'blocking gates', for example, to partition the circuit into smaller modules to ease the testing problem.

An advantge of the scan/set technique over LSSD is that the state of the

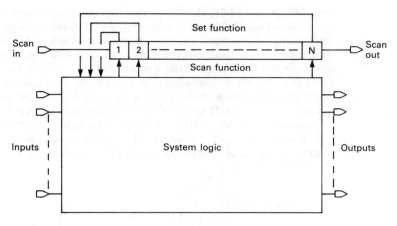

Fig. 8.4   Scan/Set configuration.[3]

system latches may be examined without interrupting the normal operation of the circuit.

8.2.3   BUILT-IN-TEST METHODS

Although LSSD techniques simplify, to some extent, the testing of complex circuits, a vast amount of test data must still be processed: input test patterns have to be generated, true value output responses computed and stored, output responses of the circuit under test stored and analysed. Several techniques have been devised in the first instance to reduce the number of test results which must be analysed to determine if a circuit is faulty. These methods are usually referred as 'data compression' techniques and include methods such as transition counting [8] and signature analysis [9]. It has been shown, however, that transition counting can produce an incorrect result, the faulty and fault-free circuit producing an identical number of zero-to-one transitions on a gate output. On the other hand, the signature analysis method has proved to be a useful adjunct in the testing of digital systems, particularly in systems which have a bus structured architecture; it has also been incorporated into the self-test technique developed for VLSI circuits called BILBO. [10]

Signature analysis

The main functional element used in signature analysis is the Linear Feedback Shift Register (LFSR) [22], which comprises, as shown in Fig. 8.5, a series of latches in which signal taps are taken from certain stages, exclusive-ORed and returned to the input of the first latch; this configuration will generate a repetitive PN (pseudo-random noise) sequence of length 2^N-1, where N is the number of latches. If the output of the exclusive-OR gate is not returned directly to the input of the first stage but is subsequently exclusive-ORed with a signal from some other source, as shown in Fig. 8.6, then at any time the contents of the register will not contain the values defined by the PN sequence, but will be modified in some way characteristic of the signal coming from the other source. This modified bit pattern contained in the register is called the 'signature' of the input source. Thus if the LFSR is initialized to a given pattern and then mixed with a signal coming from a node in a fault-free circuit, after a prescribed number of clock cycles, say 50, a signature characteristic of the fault-free circuit will be stored in the LFSR. If a similar procedure is repeated with a signal from a faulty circuit, then after the prescribed number of cycles a signature will be left in the LFSR which differs from the fault-free signature, permitting the faulty circuit to be identified. It is seen using this technique that the output data to be analysed is compressed into a single N-bit word, removing the necessity of comparing fifty output responses from the faulty and fault-free circuits.

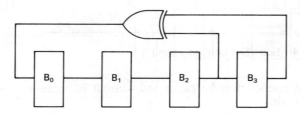

Fig. 8.5   PN sequence gen.

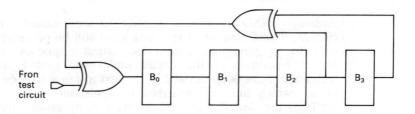

Fig. 8.6   Signature analysis register.

Built-in-logic block observation (BILBO) [10]

BILBO is a built-in test generation scheme which uses signature analysis in conjunction with a scan path. The major component in this self-test technique is a multi-mode shift register, shown in Fig. 8.7, called a BILBO, whose function is determined by two mode control lines B_1 and B_2. In practice the latches in the BILBOs are the normal system latches in the circuit, as shown in Fig. 8.8, where the Z-inputs are the outputs coming from the preceding combinational block and the Q-outputs are the inputs to the succeeding combinational block. The BILBO blocks partition the system, for the purposes of testing, into smaller subfunctions in a similar way to the SRL blocks used in LSSD.

The control lines B_1 and B_2 control the function of the BILBO in the following way.

(1) $B_1 = B_2 = 0$: the BILBO is configured into a long shift register forming a scan path.

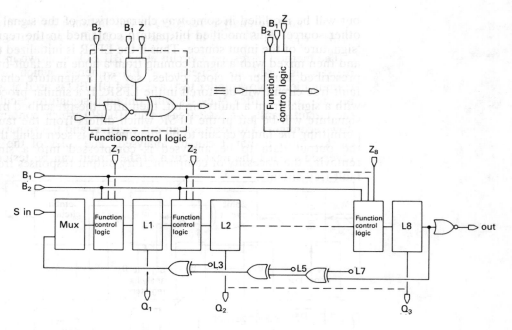

Fig. 8.7 BILBO register.

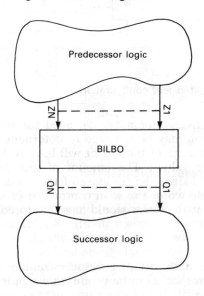

Fig. 8.8 BILBO in circuit.

(2) $B_1 = B_2 = 1$: the BILBO functions as a set of system latches in which the Z-inputs are made available to the Q-outputs for normal circuit operation.

(3) $B_1 = 1$, $B_2 = 0$: the BILBO is configured into a LFSR, resembling a

signature analysis register, in this instance having multiple inputs.

(4) $B_1 = 0$, $B_1 = 1$: in this case the BILBO register is reset.

The method of testing a circuit using BILBOs is shown in Fig. 8.9, a BILBO register is used to generate a PN-sequence which is applied to the combinational block under test; a second BILBO is used as a signature analysis register, which after N cycles will contain a signature peculiar to the state of the circuit (faulty or fault-free). The BILBO which contains the signature is now reconfigured to form a scan-out register, and the signature is subsequently clocked out so that it can be analysed. The roles of the BILBOs are then reversed so that the next section of the circuit can be tested.

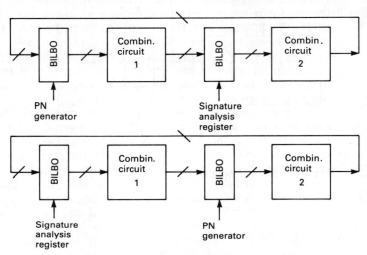

Fig. 8.9   BILBOs in a built-in test configuration.

This technique effectively eliminates the need for test pattern generation, although fault simulation may be required to determine the fault coverage of the PN-sequences; furthermore the circuit will have to be simulated to obtain the fault-free signature values. The amount of test data to be stored and analysed is also reduced since the response of the circuit to N test patterns is compressed into a single word; this is in contrast to LSSD where, say, N test patterns and subsequent responses would have to stored and analysed.

Syndrome testing [12]

The clasical methods of test pattern generation require sets of input patterns and associated output responses to be produced which involves the processing of vast amounts of data.

Another self-test technique which bypasses these problems is called 'syndrome' testing. The syndrome of a circuit is defined as $S = M/2^N$, where M is the number of minterms in the Boolean expression for the circuit and N is the number of inputs.

Consider the function,

$$W\bar{X}Y + \bar{W}X\bar{Y} + W\bar{X}Z + \bar{W}X\bar{Z} + WYZ$$

This function has six minterms, hence $S = 6/2^4 = 3/8$.

A 'syndrome' is thus a functional characteristic of a circuit independent of its realization. The concept underlying syndrome testing is to exhaustively apply all input combinations to the circuit and to count the number of 1s appearing on the output; therefore the input test vector generator for syndrome testing simply comprises an N-bit counter eliminating the need to use involved test pattern generation algorithms to produce the input patterns. Furthermore, the output data is compressed into a single word, containing the number of 1s appearing on a given output.

Not all circuits, however, are syndrome testable [13], that is certain circuits can have a single stuck-at-one or zero fault and produce an identical syndrome to the fault-free circuit; these syndrome-untestable circuits usually contain exclsuive-OR gates or reconvergent fanout paths which have an odd number of inversions along the paths. Several techniques have been evolved to make these types to circuit syndrome testable. The first technique increases the size of certain minterms in the Boolean expression by introducing a control input line which is held at a non-dominant logic value during the normal operation of the circuit but is considered as a primary input to the circuit during testing. Algorithms have been devised to determine the minimal number of control lines necessary to make a circuit syndrome testable. The cost of the additional hardware, that is the AND gates used to increase the size of the product terms, and also the extra control inputs to make the circuit syndrome testable, may be unacceptable; in such circumstances an alternative approach called 'constrained' syndrome testing [14] may be used. In this technique sections of the circuit are desensitized by holding certain inputs at fixed logic values; in this way particular internal signal lines which make the complete circuit syndrome untestable are de-activated, the resulting residual function being syndrome testable. Thus by applying several 'constrained' syndrome tests to partitions in the circuit the complete circuit can be syndrome tested.

The main disadvantage encountered when applying syndrome testing to VLSI circuits is the large size of the input counter, which results in long test times for the circuit. However, by identifying disjoint partitions in the circuit which can be tested in parallel the length of the input counter can thus be reduced with a subsequent reduction in test time. When partitioning the circuit a decision must be made on the size of the subfunctions, that is, whether to have many small subfunctions each of which can be tested quickly or few but large subfunctions which require a longer testing time. The decision is based usually on the amount of additional hardware required to create the disjoint partitions. Circuits designed using the LSSD technique can be readily adapted for syndrome testing; the SRL blocks which automatically partition the circuit into subfunctions can also be reconfigured to act as test pattern generators and syndrome registers.

Testing using Radamacher–Walsh coefficients [15]

The Radamacher–Walsh (RW) Coefficients of a logic function define the function as uniquely as a truth table. If the number of inputs is n, the number of coefficients is 2^n. In general the first $n+1$ coefficients (primary coefficients) are sufficient to detect all distinguishable faults at the output of a circuit; however, recourse to the secondary coefficients is necessary in some situations.

For any given function $F(X_1, X_2, \ldots, X_n)$ the spectral coefficients can be obtained as follows:

$$R = T_N F$$

where R is a column matrix of spectral coefficients.

F is a column matrix of output values of the circuit.

T_n is a $2^n \times 2^m$ transform matrix defined by

$$T_n = \begin{bmatrix} T_{n-1} & T_{n-1} \\ T_{n-1} & -T_{n-1} \end{bmatrix} \; ; \qquad T_0 = 1$$

Consider the function $F(X_1, X_2, X_3) = X_1 \bar{X}_3 + \bar{X}_1 X_2 X_3$.

$$
\begin{array}{ccc}
R & T_n & F
\end{array}
$$

$$
\begin{bmatrix} r_0 \\ r_1 \\ r_2 \\ r_{12} \\ r_3 \\ r_{13} \\ r_{23} \\ r_{123} \end{bmatrix}
=
\begin{bmatrix}
1 & 1 & 1 & 1 & 1 & 1 & 1 & 1 \\
1 & -1 & 1 & -1 & 1 & -1 & 1 & -1 \\
1 & 1 & -1 & -1 & 1 & 1 & -1 & -1 \\
1 & -1 & -1 & 1 & 1 & -1 & -1 & 1 \\
1 & 1 & 1 & 1 & -1 & -1 & -1 & -1 \\
1 & -1 & 1 & -1 & -1 & 1 & -1 & 1 \\
1 & 1 & -1 & -1 & -1 & -1 & 1 & 1 \\
1 & -1 & -1 & 1 & -1 & 1 & 1 & -1
\end{bmatrix}
\cdot
\begin{bmatrix} 0 \\ 1 \\ 0 \\ 1 \\ 1 \\ 0 \\ 0 \\ 0 \end{bmatrix}
=
\begin{bmatrix} 3 \\ -1 \\ 1 \\ 1 \\ 1 \\ -3 \\ -1 \\ -1 \end{bmatrix}
$$

From the value of R the Radamacher–Walsh spectral response can be plotted. To illustrate the effect of a fault on the RW coefficients, consider the function $F = (X_2 + X_3) X_1 + X_1 X_4$.

$$
\begin{bmatrix} r_0 \\ r_1 \\ r_2 \\ r_{12} \\ r_3 \\ r_{13} \\ r_{23} \\ r_{123} \\ r_4 \\ r_{14} \\ r_{24} \\ r_{124} \\ r_{34} \\ r_{134} \\ r_{234} \\ r_{1234} \end{bmatrix}
=
\begin{bmatrix} T_n \end{bmatrix}
\cdot
\begin{bmatrix} 0 \\ 0 \\ 0 \\ 1 \\ 0 \\ 1 \\ 0 \\ 1 \\ 1 \\ 0 \\ 1 \\ 1 \\ 1 \\ 1 \\ 1 \\ 1 \end{bmatrix}
=
\begin{bmatrix} 10 \\ -2 \\ -2 \\ 1 \\ -2 \\ 2 \\ -2 \\ 2 \\ -4 \\ -4 \\ 0 \\ 0 \\ 0 \\ 0 \\ 0 \\ 0 \end{bmatrix}
$$

If X_3 is stuck-at-1, that is $F^1 = X_1 + \bar{X}_1 X_4$

$$
\begin{bmatrix}
r_0 \\
r_1 \\
r_2 \\
r_{12} \\
r_3 \\
r_{13} \\
r_{23} \\
r_{123} \\
r_4 \\
r_{14} \\
r_{24} \\
r_{124} \\
r_{34} \\
r_{134} \\
r_{234} \\
r_{1234}
\end{bmatrix}
=
\begin{bmatrix}
T_n
\end{bmatrix}
\cdot
\begin{bmatrix}
0 \\
1 \\
0 \\
1 \\
0 \\
1 \\
0 \\
1 \\
1 \\
1 \\
1 \\
1 \\
1 \\
1 \\
1 \\
1
\end{bmatrix}
=
\begin{bmatrix}
12 \\
-4 \\
0 \\
0 \\
0 \\
0 \\
0 \\
0 \\
-4 \\
-4 \\
0 \\
0 \\
0 \\
0 \\
0 \\
0
\end{bmatrix}
$$

In the spectral response, any large positive value except r_0 means that the output is strongly dependent upon the positive value of that input, a large negative value means that the inverse of that signal value has a strong influence on the output. If a primary spectral coefficient is zero, it implies that the line is syndrome untestable and recourse to the secondary coefficients is made which essentially measures the correlation between inputs. Thus when a fault exists it is possible to determine the location of the fault by observing which spectral values are affected. It should be noted that alterations in the spectra, brought about by some fault condition, are unlikely to be arithmetic except in the very restricted cases where inputs are disjoint.

The concept underlying the use of RW spectra to determine if a circuit is faulty is to create a signature for the fault-free circuit in terms of the RW coefficients, which in the presence of a fault condition will change value. This technique is very similar to syndrome testing, which essentially determines the value of the r_0 spectral value, which is the number of 1s appearing in the output function.

The hardware required to test a circuit by means of the RW coefficients, shown in Fig. 8.10, comprises a high-speed counter to generate all possible input combinations; a Walsh coefficient generator, which is a simple multiplexer, if testing can be done using only the primary coefficients, i.e. $r_0, \ldots, r_n$ or, if secondary coefficients are required, an exclusive-OR tree; and a coefficient accumulator; a separate test is run for each coefficient in the signature.

8.3 Testability analysis

Testability analysis attempts to quantify the testability properties, usually, of

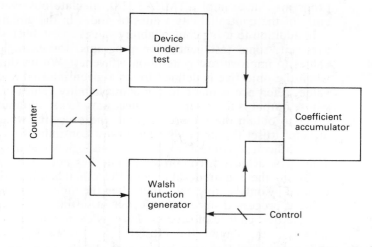

Fig. 8.10   Built-in Radamacher Walsh coefficient test architecture.[13]

an unstructured circuit design, identifying nodes in the circuit whose logic values are difficult to control or observe, test points are then located at these nodes or that section of the circuit is redesigned to simplify testing. Testability measurements can either be 'extrinsic' or 'intrinsic'; extrinsic measurement of testability is derived from the fault coverage and requires a knowledge of both circuit structure and associated test sequences. Intrinsic measurement of testability, however, is derived directly from the structure of the circuit without any recourse to input/output response of the circuit.

In the past a coarse estimate of the testability of a circuit was obtained simply by scrutinizing a design for particular characteristics which from past experience proved difficult to test, for example buried flip flops which could not be set or reset easily. However, to obtain a more accurate testability profile of a circuit algorithmic approaches have been developed which operate on the circuit topology. In determining the testability profile of a circuit two figures of merit are calculated for each node: its controllability and observability. The controllability of a node is a measure of the ease with which it can be set to a particular logic value by assigning logic values to the primary inputs of the circuit. In some systems different controllability figures are calculated depending upon the logic value to which the node is to be set. The observability of a node is a measure of the ease with which the condition of the node can be observed at a primary output of the circuit; the observability figure implicitly includes a measure of the controllability of the nodes instrumental in sensitizing a path from the given node to a primary output. The testability figure for each node is derived from the product of these two values.

Several testability analysis programs have been developed, and although their objective is the same the programs differ in the rigour of the analysis that is performed on the circuit. For example, CAMELOT [16] does not distinguish between the controllability figures for setting a node to a logic one or logic zero, which is in contrast to SCOAP [17] which not only derives different controllability values for setting a node to 0 or 1 but also distinguishes between combinational and sequential controllabilities and observabilities. Other programs, for example, TMEAS [18] calculate observability values independently of the controllability values of nodes in the circuit.

In addition to using controllability values to establish the testability profile of a circuit, some test generation programs, for example PODEM, use these values to improve test generation efficiency. Within the PODEM procedures, when the objective is defined to set a given internal node to a particular logic value, reference is made to the controllability values of the inputs to the gate whose output is to be set. If it is necessary to set all inputs to a definite value in order to obtain the required output, the objective which is then defined is to attempt to set the input with the lowest controllability value, that is the input most difficult to control, to the required logic value first, since if this objective cannot be achieved, computation time has not been wasted setting the other inputs to the required value. On the other hand, if the gate output can be defined by only setting one input, then the input with the highest controllability value is processed since the objective of setting this input to the required value has the best chance of success. Thus by examining the controllability values of nodes in the circuit the efficiency of the test generation process can be increased.

8.4 Examples of standard cell components and gate arrays with built in test features

Until recently, design techniques to enhance testability could only be incorporated, readily, into full custom designed circuits. However, several companies have now developed standard cell components and gate arrays which include features to enhance the testability of complete designs.

In response to the requirements of the system designer for a microcontroller which could be customized for a specific application, Intel produced a SuperCel Design System [19] which comprises a microcontroller supercell whose function can be made applicaton specific by modifying the peripheral logic which includes standard cells (basic gates), high-level cells (registers, decoders, etc.) and high-density array cells (ROM, RAMs, PLAs). In order to test the microcontroller core independently of the peripheral customizing logic some test hardware was incorporated into the microcontroller supercell in the form of an 'isolation' ring; during test mode the microcontroller can be disconnected from the peripheral logic and tested as a stand alone component, thereafter the microcontroller core is used to test the peripheral logic.

CDC have also included some built-in test features into their 6K gate array [20], based on the BILBO technique. The array contains three additional registers for testing purposes, that is an input register, an output register and a control register. The input and output registers are used as either a data source or sink for nodes between the primary inputs/outputs of the circuit and the internal gate array. The control register simply regulates the function of the input/output registers, which are essentially in parallel with the primary input/output lines to the logic array, consequently there is no performance penalty by incorporating the built-in test logic on the chip. The circuit can be configured into a self-test mode in which the primary inputs are disabled and the input register is converted to pseudo-random number generator which supplies the test vectors for the logic array. The output register is configured into a checksum register and accepts outputs directly from the logic array or the output buffers. The additional test hardware on the chip can also be used to perform interconnect tests between chips on a printed circuit board, since patterns can be loaded into the output register of one chip and transmitted to the input registers of the other chips on the board to which it is connected, thus permitting open and shorted interconnections on the printed circuit board to be located.

References

1. Grason, J. and Nagle, A.W. Digital test generation and design for testability. *17th Design Automation Conference Proceedings*, 175–89 (1980).
2. Williams, T.W. Design for testability. *Proc. NATO Advanced Study Institute on Computer Aided Design for VLSI Circuits* (Italy) (1980).
3. Stewart, J.H. Future testing of large LSI circuit cards. *Digest of Papers 1977, Semiconductor Test Symposium*, 6–15 (1977).
4. Hisashige, A. Testing VLSI with random access scan. *Digest of Papers, Compcon '80*, 50–2 (1980).
5. Bhavsar, D.K. Design for test calculus — an algorithm for DFT rule checking. *20th Design Automation Conference Proceedings*, 300–7 (1983).
6. Bennetts, R.G. *Design of Testable Logic Circuits*, Addison-Wesley, Chapter 3 (1984).
7. Das Gupta, S. *et al.* An enhancement to LSSD and some applications of LSSD in reliability, availability and serviceability. *Proc. 11th Fault Tolerant Computing Symposium*, 32–4 (1981).
8. Breuer, M.A. and Friedman, A.D. *Diagnosis and Reliable Design of Digital Systems*. Pitman, 152–6 (1977).
9. Hewlett-Packard. *A Designer's Guide to Signature Analysis*, Applications Note 222 (1977).
10. Koenemann, B., Mucha, J. and Zwiehoff, G. Built-in logic block observation techniques. *Digest of Papers, 1979 Test Conference*, 37–41 (1979).
11. Smith, J.E. Measure of the effectiveness of fault signature analysis. *IEEE Trans. Computers*, C-29(6), 510–14 (1980).
12. Savir, J. Syndrome-testable design of combinational circuits. *IEEE Trans. Computers*, C-29(6), 442–51 (1980).
13. Muzio, J.C. and Miller, D.M. Spectral technique for fault detection. *Proc. 12th Fault Tolerant Computing Symposium*, 297–302 (1982).
14. Savir, J. Syndrome testing of 'syndrome-untestable' combinational circuits. *IEEE Trans. Computers*, C-30(8), 606–8 (1981).
15. Susskind, A.K. Testing by verifying walsh coefficients. *Proc. 11th Fault Tolerant Computing Symposium*, 206–8 (1981).
16. Bennetts, R.G., Maunder, C.M. and Robinson, G.D. Camelot: a computer aided measure for logic testability. *Proc. IEE*, **128** (Part E, No. 5), 177–189 (1981).
17. Goldstein, L.H. and Thigpen, E.L. Scoap: Sandia Controllability/Observability Analysis Program. *17th Design Automation Conference Proceedings*, 190–6 (1980).
18. Grason, J. TMEAS — a testability measurement program. *16th Design Automation Conference Proceedings*, 156–61 (1979).
19. Koehler, R. Design a microcontroller 'Supercell' for testability. *VLSI Design*, 44–6 (1983).
20. Resnick, D.R. Testability and maintainability with a new 6K gate array. *VLSI Design*, 34–8 (March/April 1983).

9 High-level languages for layout

9.1 Introduction

In the early days of IC design, methods for producing artwork were usually graphical. As design became more complex, it became obvious that a textual representation had many advantages, since it allowed the designer to design in a more structured way. Low-level languages have been available for some time for describing the layout of a chip in terms of polygons on different mask layers. [1, 2] These include CIF (Cal-tech. Intermediate Form) and Gaelic. Although syntactically different, these languages are very similar in capability, and translation between the two is easily accomplished.

The Gaelic language provides the following features:

— definition of a rectangle;
— definition of a polygon;
— definition of a group of polygons and rectangles;
— creation of a group instance (may be nested).

An example of the description of a simple shift register cell in Gaelic is shown in Fig. 9.1 and the corresponding mask layout is shown in Fig. 9.2.

Note that the butting contact is defined as a group called *PDMBUT* and used twice by the shift register cell.

Although this provides a useful level of abstraction from the geometry of the masks, it is deficient in several ways. For instance, the layer numbers and coordinates must be integer constants — this binds the description to a particular technology and line width. Also, the library facilities are poor, since only fixed blocks may be added. Hence, for example, a four-bit adder and a five-bit adder would need to be defined separately despite their similarity. The structuring is also poor — although an improvement on graphical methods, it is still difficult to express the hierarchy of a design. There are no high-level aids for tedious parts of the layout which can be automated, such as placement of the connection pads around the finished chip.

```
!    Gaelic description of a shift register cell;
*    UNITS = MICRONS , GRID = 0.1;
!    A butting contact;
NEWGROUP PDMBUT;
RECT(3)−60,−90:120,180;          RECT(5)−30,−60:60,120;
RECT(1)−60,−90:120,90;           RECT(2)−60,−30:120,120;
ENDGROUP;
!    The shift register cell group definition;
NEWGROUP SHFCLL;
RECT(5)120,540:60,60;            RECT(5)120,−30:60,60;
RECT(4)60,210:180,330;           RECT(3)0,510:630,120;
RECT(3)0,−60:630,120;            RECT(2)330,270:150,60;
RECT(2)270,240:60,90;            RECT(2)240,180:90,60;
RECT(2)90,510:120,120;           RECT(2)120,360:60,150;
RECT(2)90,300:120,60;            RECT(2)90,30:120,150;
RECT(2)210,30:30,270;            RECT(2)60,30:30,270;
RECT(2)90,−60:120,120;           RECT(1)480,90:150,60;
RECT(1)360,−60:60,690;           RECT(1)0,90:300,60;
RECT(1)60,360:180,120;           RECT(1)210,270:30,90;
RECT(1)60,270:30,90;
GROUP PDMBUT,540,240,XX ;
GROUP PDMBUT,150,270,RR ;
ENDGROUP;
!;
!The main group contains an instance of the cell;
!;
GROUP SHFCLL,0,0,XX ;
FINISH;
```

Fig. 9.1 An example of the GAELIC language.

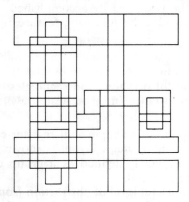

Fig. 9.2 Layout of a shift register cell.

9.2 Embedded high-level layout languages

One way to improve upon the lower-level languages is to embed procedure
calls which manipulate a layout database in a high-level programming
language. Some examples of languages of this type are as follows:

—	APECS	(based on Pascal) [3]
—	LAP	(based on Simula) [4]
—	ILAP	(based on IMP) [5]
—	PLAP	(based on Pascal) [6, 7]
—	Sticks and Stones	(based on ML)[8]

Although some of these languages also incorporate electrical and functional specification information about the design, we are concerned here only with the layout part. PLAP, which was developed at Newcastle University based on ILAP and LAP, is the subject of the remainder of this discussion, although many of the features are common to other embedded layout languages.

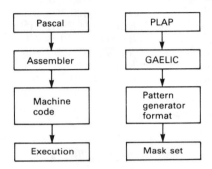

Fig. 9.3   High-level language analogy.

The analogy between programming in a high-level language and using a high-level layout language is illustrated in Fig. 9.3. Each level provides a certain amount of abstraction from the details in the level below. At the top level, the designer can work in terms of blocks which are connected together via a defined interface in terms of connection points or 'pins' on the bounding rectangles of blocks (the bounding rectangle is the smallest possible rectangle which encloses all parts of the block). This technique allows designs to be done either top-down or bottom-up, the decomposition or composition being done without regard to the detail at the lowest level, i.e. shapes on the masks. The design is eventually produced as a Gaelic mask description after processing by PLAP.

9.3   PLAP

The features of PLAP will be described in a bottom-up fashion for clarity, though top-down design is preferable in the actual design process.

9.3.1   LEAF CELL CONSTRUCTION

A leaf cell consists of the geometric primitives of the Gaelic language enclosed in a named block definition. A simple example of the design of an NMOS depletion mode transistor is shown in Fig. 9.4 and the resulting layout in Fig. 9.5. Note that the dimensions are now integral multiples of lambda and layers are given symbolic names. These will be substituted by PLAP according to the process used to implement the design.

```
(* PLAP definition of a pull-up transistor *)
define ('pullup');         (* the name of the defn. *)
    pdm(0,0,x);                        (* a poly-diff contact *)
    rect(diff,−1,0,2,5+4);             (* a depletion mode FET *)
    rect(implant,−3,−2,6,6+4);
    rect(poly,–3,0,6,6);
enddef;
```

Fig. 9.4 PLAP description of a leaf cell.

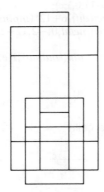

Fig. 9.5 PLAP leaf cell: a pull-up transistor.

As many cells can be defined as are desired, the restrictions being that definition names must be unique in the first six characters (a Gaelic limitation) and definitions may not be nested.

9.3.2 COMPOSITE CELL CONSTRUCTION

Composite cells contain both geometric primitives and instances of other cells (composite or leaf). An example of a composite cell is shown in Figs 9.6 and 9.7. This simple NMOS NOR gate is made from a leaf cell (pull-down transistor) and a composite cell (inverter) which is itself made from a pull-up and pull-down transistor. Some geometric primitives are used to provide interconnections.

The connection points of this cell are identified by the PIN procedure. This allows some of the interconnection to be automated and provides a means of abstraction to a 'block diagram' representation of the block.

9.3.3 PARAMETERIZATION AND REPETITION

The definition of the gate in Fig. 9.6 is done by calling a parameterized Pascal procedure which can generate a gate with an arbitrary number of inputs. The PLAP procedures which create the definition of the gate are called from inside

```
procedure define_nor(name:string; inpins:integer);
var
    i : integer
begin
if inpins>3 then writeln('Warning — unusually large fan-in');
define(name);
    for i:=1 to inpins−1 do
        begin
        instance('pulldn','noripd',i,6+12*(i−1),0,xx);
        rect(poly,10+12*(i−1),−4,2,9);
        dm(6+12*(i−1),0);
        pin('input',i,s,11+12*(i−1),1);
        end;
    instance('invert','norinv',1,6+12*(inpins−1),0,xx);
    rect(poly,12+12*(inpins−1),−4,2,9);   rect(diff,6+12*(inpins−1),6,6,2);
    rect(diff,6,6,6+12*(inpins−1),2);      rect(metal,0,−2,12+12*(inpins−1),4);
    rect(metal,0,16,12+12*(inpins−1),4);
    pin('input', inpins,s,11+12*(inpins−1),1);   pin('output',1,e,7,2);
    pin('vdd',1,w,18,3);pin('vdd',2e,18,3);
    pin('vss',1,w,0,3);pin('vss',2,e,0,3);
enddef;
end;
```

Fig. 9.6   PLAP description of a composite cell.

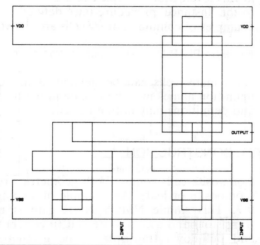

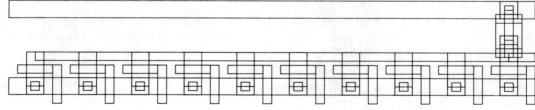

Fig. 9.7   PLAP composite cells: NOR gates with 2 and 10 inputs.

125 / High-level languages for layout

the procedure *define_nor*. This also illustrates the use of a loop to generate the appropriate number of instances of the pull-down transistor. Each block instance and pin has both a name and a number which identify it uniquely within a definition. The number allows multiple instances to be specified uniquely in a loop without generating new instance names for every circuit of the loop.

The use of parameterized procedures to generate definitions is a powerful one, since it allows blocks to be recursively defined. For example, an *n*-bit multiplier can be defined in terms of *n*/2-bit multipliers, the procedure which generates the *n*-bit multiplier calling itself with a smaller value for *n* to generate smaller multipliers. Eventually, the recursion reaches a point where *n* is small enough for the multiplier to be defined as an instance of a PLA. At each stage of the recursion, the appropriate adders to combine the partial products and the interconnections are inserted in the definition.

9.3.4 LIBRARY CELLS

The procedure library facilities of the programming language used enable cell libraries to be generated. Common leaf cells such as contacts may be instanced directly by a special procedure call once defined by a library cell, since the full instance call is usually not required — instance names are usually not desirable at this level. More complex cells may be instanced in the normal way by a call to the 'instance' procedure once defined by a call to a library procedure. Some examples of common library cells are shown in Fig. 9.8. The Xerox library cells

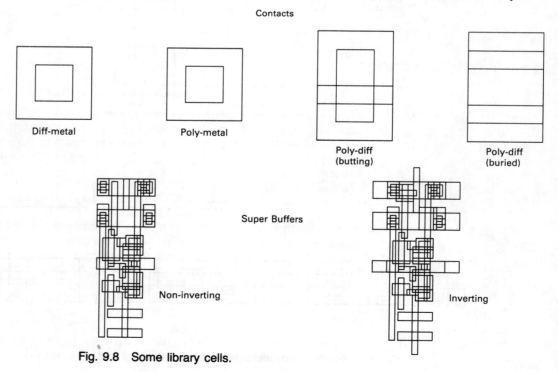

Fig. 9.8   Some library cells.

are available as part of the built-in PLAP library. Other parameterized cells contributed by users include ALU slices, registers, decoders and so on.

9.3.5 PROGRAMMABLE STRUCTURES

PLA definitions can be created automatically from a bit table produced by a PLA minimizer program [7] by calling a library procedure. An example of this using the Mead and Conway traffic light controller example [1] is shown in Figs 9.9 and 9.10. The bit table is specified by giving the name of the bit table file produced by the minimizer. This illustrates another useful feature of PLAP — the ability to read and write external data files during the layout process. The ability to produce PLAs automatically allows many types of combinational logic blocks and FSM controllers to be produced with little effort.

```
[inherit('$plap:.inc')]
program example_pla;
var
    ins,outs,feeds:integer;
begin
    initialize('traffic.lng');
    (* Create a definition of a PLA by a call to a *)
    (* library procedure. The filename is given    *)
    (* as the string 'traffic.pla' .               *)
    makepla('ex','traffic.pla',ins,outs,feeds);
    finish('ex')
end.
```

Fig. 9.9   PLAP description of a PLA.

9.3.6 INTERCONNECTION

Three methods are available for connection blocks together.

— Abutment — this requires the connection points to be matched along the edges to be abutted. Blocks which are to be hidden internally for the purposes of abstraction must have sufficient spacing between internal structures and the bounding box to prevent design rule violations during abutment.

— Manual routing — it is possible to obtain the coordinates of a pin and route it manually using geometric primitives. This is normally of use only at the lowest levels of the hierarchy.

— Automatic routing — the auto-routers currently in use are not able to route around blocks — they must be given a clean rectangle in which to work. Pins of blocks whose edges define such a rectangle can be linked together by specifying them as part of a net by calls to the *net, netpin* and *endnet* procedures. When all the nets have been defined, routing is done by a call to one of four procedures, depending on the topology of the net. Some routers use only one layer, others use two. The choice of router is determined by the factors shown in Table 9.1. Use of the four automatic routers in PLAP is demonstrated in the example shown in Figs 9.11 and 9.12.

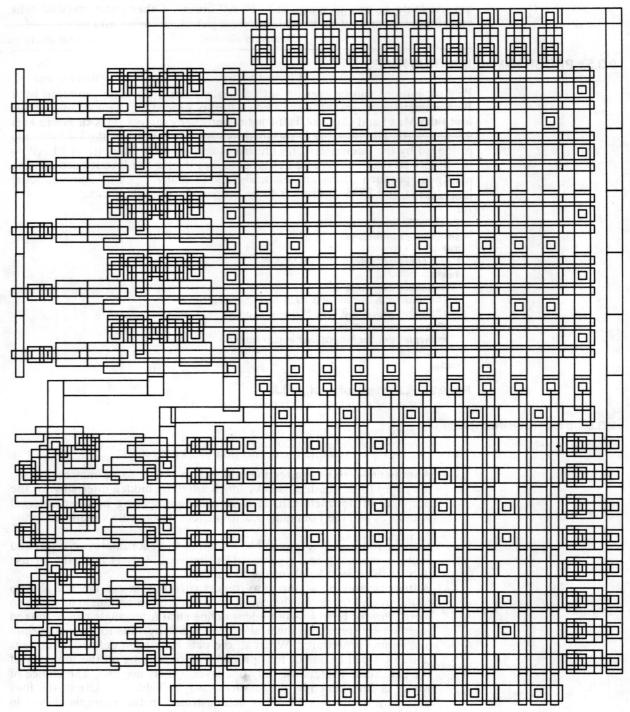

Fig. 9.10 The Mead and Conway traffic light PLA.

Table 9.1   Choice of Auto-Router

	Crossovers allowed	No crossovers
Between two parallel sides	Channel router	River router
Between all four sides	Two layer router	One layer router

```
[inherit)'$plap:.inc')]
program routedemo;
var
   d,i,pinrep,j,xmin,ymin,xinc,yinc : integer;
begin
   initialize('exroute');
   { *** DEFINITIONS SECTION *** }
   define_contacts;
   define_pads;
   define('blocka');
      boundbox(0,0,200,200);
      ⋮
      (* create pins on boundary *)
      ⋮
      end;
   enddef;
(* blockb and blockc defined similarly *)
   { *** CHIP DEFINITION SECTION *** }
   define('rblock');
      { *** place instances of major blocks *** }
      instance('blocka','blocka',1,0,200,xx);
      ⋮
      instance('blockc','blockc',1,−15,−250,xx);
      { *** define connections for the ONE-LAYER router *** }
      for j:=1 to 2 do begin
        for i:=1 to 4 do begin
           net('netnol',i+4*(j−1),2);
              netpin('blocka',j,'pinpo1',i);
              netpin('blockb',j,'pinpl2',i);
           endnet
        end;
        onelayroute(poly)
      end;
      { *** define connections for the TWO-LAYER router *** }
      { *** define connections using the CHANNEL router *** }
      { *** connect input pads using the RIVER router *** }
      { *** connect output pads using the RIVER router *** }
   enddef;
   finish('rblock')
end.
```

Fig. 9.11   A PLAP description using auto-routing.

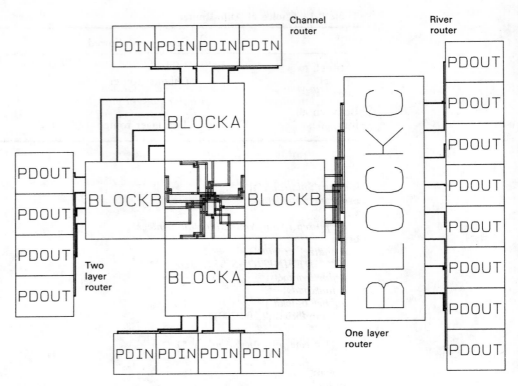

Fig. 9.12   A plot showing routing in PLAP.

9.3.7   PAD PLACEMENT

When a design has been finished and must be connected to the outside world, connection pads for inputs, outputs, and power must be placed around the design. Special procedures are available for placing and connecting these pads, which are nearly identical to the pads in the Xerox library. (Some changes are necessary to allow auto-routing). The design is specified as a block with pins which are to be linked to pads on the edges, and the pads are placed around this by calls the the procedures *placepads* and *padselect*. The pads are connected by calls to *padpin*. A call to *endplacepads* completes the placement and routing of the pads. Connection of power between pads is done automatically. The use of the pad placement procedure is shown in Figs 9.13 and 9.14.

9.3.8   ADDITIONAL FEATURES

Several features have been included in PLAP as aids to the designer, some of which are listed below.

(1)   Annotation — text may be produced as polygons on the masks — this is useful for labelling chips.

```
[inherit ('$plap:.inc')]
program plachip;
const
    minspace = 7;   {distance between contacts}
    sideexten = 7;   {side extension on I/O box around PLA for clock signals}
var
    i,j.mxin,ymin,xinc,yinc,xdisp,ydisp,xl,yl,ioexten,
    nins,nouts,nfeeds,maxio,plawidth,plaheight,plabase : integer;
begin
    initialize('plachip');
    cells;
    {**** Read in the PLA table and set up the definition ****}
        ⋮
    {**** Instance the PLA and define the pad placement box ****}
    define('plablk');
        ⋮
    enddef;
    {**** Select and place the I/O pads around the PLA box ****}
    placepads('plablk','plachp');
        padselect('pdclkb',1,n);
            padpin('ckl1',1,'clki',1,4);
            padpin('clk2',1,'clko',1,4);
        padselect('pdvdd',1,s);
            padpin('vdd',3,'vdd',1,4);
        padselect('pdgnd',1,2);
            padpin('gnd',1,'gnd',1,4);
        for i:=1 to nins do begin
            padselect('pdin',i,w);
                padpin('input',1,'input',i,4)
        end;
        for i:=1 to nouts do begin
            padselect('pdout',i,e);
                padpin('output',output',1,'output',i4)
        end;
    endplacepads;
    finish('plachp')
end.
```

Fig. 9.13 A PLAP description using pad placement.

(2) Process features changes — changes of mask numbers, the value of lambda and the type of contact (butting or buried) may be performed to customize the output for a particular fabrication process.

(3) Creation of empty boxes — this can be useful in top-down design where the internal details can be filled in later once the floorplan has been created.

9.4 Conclusions

PLAP brings many of the features of a high-level programming language into use to aid the layout of a chip. Flexible, parameterized blocks can be called as procedures and cells can be used without detailed knowledge of their internal

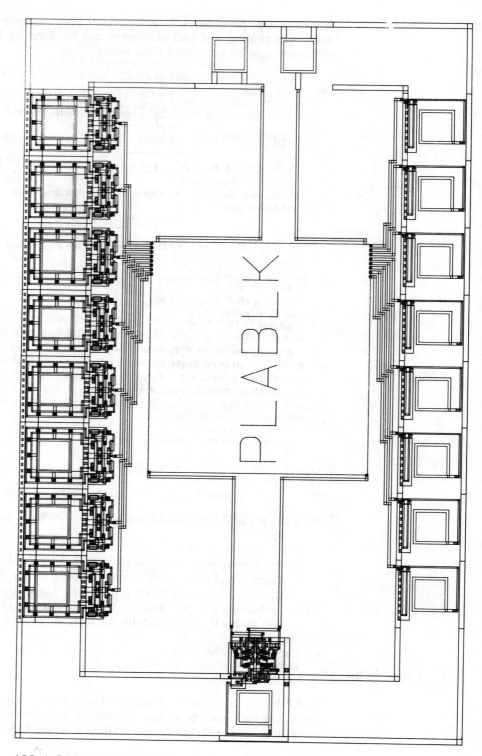

Fig. 9.14 An example of automatic pad placement.

structure (cf. procedures in a high-level programming language). Low-level tasks like routing and pad placement can be done by PLAP. Programmable structures can be generated from tables.

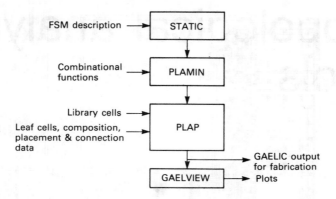

Fig. 9.15 Design route using PLAP.

A typical design route using PLAP is shown in Fig. 9.15. After the design has been decomposed into the fundamental components, the controller parts can be designed as synchronous PLA FSMs using STATIC.[7] The combinational PLAs can be defined by Boolean equations and then minimized. Devices such as registers etc. can be called from a PLAP library. The placement and interconnection information are provided in the PLAP description, and then, finally, the PLAP program is run to generate a Gaelic description ready for viewing or mask generation.

References

1. Mead, C.A. and Conway, L.A. *Introduction to VLSI Systems*. Addison-Wesley (1980).
2. Science Research Council, *An Introductory Guide to the GAELIC Language* (1980).
3. Boyd, D.R.S. *APECS: A Pascal Environment for Circuit Specification*. Internal Memo, Rutherford Appleton Laboratories, Chilton, Didcot, 1981.
4. Locanthi, B. *LAP: A SIMULA Package for I.C. Layout*. Cal. Tech. Display File No. 1862 (1978).
5. *VLSI Design Tools*. Computer Science Dept., Edinburgh University (1983).
6. Dlay, S.S. *Integrated Circuit Layout Techniques Using Procedures Embedded in Pascal*. Ph.D. Thesis, Newcastle University (1984).
7. *VLSI Design Tools*. Dept. of Elect. Eng., Newcastle University (1983).
8. Cardelli, L. *The Sticks and Stones Painter's Manual*. Computer Science Dept., Edinburgh University (1980).

10 Topological analysis tools

10.1 Introduction

Topological analysis tools were developed initially out of necessity rather than part of some structured CAD methodology. Their function is essentially to analyse a layout comprising many thousands of geometric shapes for design rule errors, so relieving the tedium and the uncertainty of performing these checks manually. However, as design styles evolved away from complete manual layout methods the need for some of the analysis tools diminished; for example, the use of dynamic symbolic layout methods [1] removed the need to perform intra-cell dimension rule checks, since this is implicitly performed in the compaction procedure associated with symbolic layout techniques; the use of standard cells with automatic layout removes the necessity to perform a layout to function check, since the data for simulation and layout are derived from a common input description language, and if the circuit produces the required response during simulation, this implies that the function·inter-connectivity used by the autolayout program is also correct. The use of hierarchical design techniques incorporating a 'bottom-up' implementation removes the necessity of performing global design rule checks, thus reducing the amount of data to be processed at any one time.

Topological analysis programs have been developed to perform the following functions:

(1) dimension rule checking;
(2) device and function recognition;
(3) connectivity checking;
(4) electrical rule checking;
(5) electrical parameter extraction.

The kernel of these analysis programs is a set of functions which perform dimensional (sizing, calculation of areas), topological (enclosure, overlap, abuttment) and logical (AND, OR, etc.) operations on the shapes in the layout.

10.2 Dimension rule checking

The most widely used topological analysis tool is the dimension rule checker (DRC), whose function is to examine the shapes in a layout to determine such attributes as their dimensions and areas and also to establish topological relationships between shapes on one or more mask levels in the layout.

The necessity to enforce dimension rules on a layout arises from limitations in the manufacturing process in general, for example the inability to accurately resolve small line widths during mask making, to align masks during processing or to control the chemical processes. Consequently, if a reasonable yield is to be obtained, the layout must comply to a set of proven dimension rules for a given fabrication process.

The basic set of dimension rule checks performed upon a layout comprises the following:

(1) checks on minimum feature width, minimum spacing between shapes on the same or different mask levels, inter-limb spacing and calculation of areas;

(2) topological checks to determine whether shapes, either on the same or different mask levels, overlap, abut or enclose each other;

(3) relational rule checks which establish the relationship between the dimensions of a given shape, for example, aspect ratios of a device.

Although some of the individual checks performd on a layout are trivial in themselves, the major problem with DRC when applied to large layouts is the overall number of checks which must be performed; consequently much research has been directed towards developing techniques which reduce the amount of computer time required to perform a DRC by limiting the amount of data which must be processed at any one time.

In the past, a simple test — for example, checking the separation between shapes on the same mask level — would be performed by checking each shape against every other shape on that mask level, which for N shapes results in N^2 checks, and is obviously wasteful of computing time since a shape located in the bottom left-hand corner of a layout is unlikely to violate a separation design rule with a shape in the top right-hand corner; furthermore, when shape A has been compared with shape B, there is no requirement to check shape B against shape A, this wastage of computer time is further increased if the geometries considered are complex polygons rather than simple rectangles. Several techniques have been developed to reduce the amount of CPU time required to perform a given design rule check by either reducing the complexity of the shapes involved or by reducing the amount of data processed in performing the check.

10.2.1 TECHNIQUES FOR IMPROVING THE EFFICIENCY OF DRC RUN-TIMES [2]

(a) *Reduction of shape complexity*. Within the data structure used to store the description of the shapes in the layout, in addition to the coordinates of the vertices of the shapes, those of the bounding rectangle of the shape are stored. These bounding rectangles are subsequently used, as shown in Fig. 10.1, to reduce the amount of effort involved in checking for design rule violations between complex polygons. One of the bounding rectangles is inflated by the minimum allowable separation between shapes, and if the boundary rectangles do not overlap then no further processing is required; in this way the amount of unnecessary analysis is reduced.

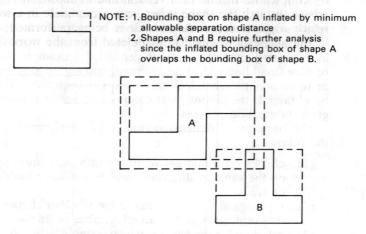

NOTE: 1. Bounding box on shape A inflated by minimum allowable separation distance
2. Shapes A and B require further analysis since the inflated bounding box of shape A overlaps the bounding box of shape B.

Fig. 10.1 Simplification of shape comparisons with bounding boxes.

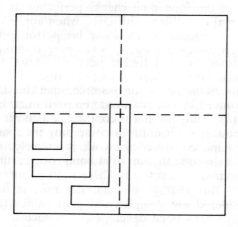

Fig. 10.2 Data partitioning using sub-areas.

(b) *Static partitioning of data.* In this technique the layout is partitioned into sub-areas, as shown in Fig. 10.2, and in any design rule check only the shapes inside a given sub-area are processed. Care, however, must be exercised when considering shapes which straddle area boundaries, since these will be involved in the checks applied in adjacent areas. The major problem with this technique is to determine the optimum size of the sub-areas, since if the areas are too extensive a large number of shapes are involved in each test, and if they are too small many shapes have to be included in checks in the adjacent sub-area. This technique assumes that the data structure used to store the layout description is 'area oriented'.

136 / CAD for VLSI

(c) *Dynamic partitioning of data.* In this technique the layout data must be ordered in terms of the coordinates of the bottom left-hand corner of the bounding rectangle of the shape. It is then assumed that the layout is scanned by either a horizontal or a vertical line as shown in Fig. 10.3. If the scan line passes through the shape it becomes a candidate in a work list of shapes upon which a given design rule check is being performed; as the line scans, the layout shapes are added to or deleted from the work list.

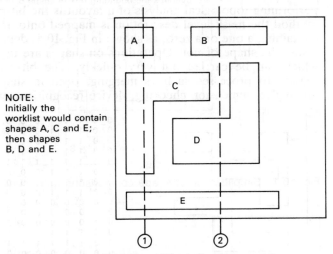

NOTE:
Initially the worklist would contain shapes A, C and E; then shapes B, D and E.

Fig. 10.3 Dynamic data partitioning using scan lines.

(d) *Exploitation of hierarchy.* In this technique the number of checks made on a layout is reduced by not analysing repeated instances of a given shape or group of shapes in a layout. Furthermore, if a 'bottom-up' implementation procedure is used it is sufficient to analyse only the relationships between the peripheral shapes of the subfunctions which are used to implement a larger function. Thus, as shown in Fig. 10.4, only one instance of subfunction A

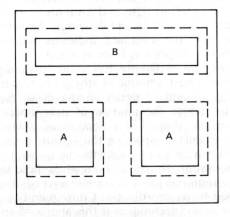

Fig. 10.4 Hierarchical dimension rule checking.

137 / Topological analysis tools

would be completely checked, and only the peripheral shapes in both instances of subfunction A and subfunction B when these are combined to form a more complex function. In addition to reducing the amount of analysis time by only checking one instance of a repetitive block, the number of error messages is also reduced.

(e) *Localization of data through bit-mapping techniques.* A recent technique developed to reduce the amount of time taken to process shapes whilst performing topological analysis of a layout is the bit-map technique.[3] In this method the mask level description is mapped onto an array of cells, each cell containing a one or a zero, as shown in Fig. 10.5, depending whether the cell is inside the shape or not. Operations on shapes are thus reduced to testing bits which can be carried out very quickly. The bit-map approach lends itself readily to processes such as merging, decomposing complex polygons into rectangles, dimension checking, device recognition, etc.

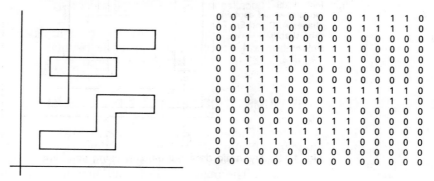

Fig. 10.5   Representation of shapes by bit maps.

When the bit-map technique is used for dimension checking it offers the additional advantage of localizing the data to be analysed, as shown in Fig. 10.6, where it is assumed that a minimum spacing check is to be performed. A square window one unit larger than the dimension being checked is passed across the layout, from left to right and from top to bottom, moving down one row at a time. The pattern of 1s and 0s within the window is observed; if the pattern '101' appears in the window it indicates that the minimum spacing of two units between the shapes has been violated.

Although the bit-map technique has many advantages, it has one major disadvantage in that a vast amount of storage is required for the mask data, independent of the amount of detail on the mask. Several techniques have been developed to reduce the amount of data stored in the bit-map. One method is to map the shapes in a section of a layout onto an 'essential coordinate' grid [4], thus compacting the layout; a second is to use variable density windows [4] whose size varies with the amount of detail contained in a given region of the layout. However, even when these techniques are used, the amount of storage required for a shape still exceeds that required by a shape when it is described by its coordinates. Consequently further work is required in bit-map data reduction techniques if this approach to topological analysis is to be exploited to its fullest potential. One technique which greatly reduces the

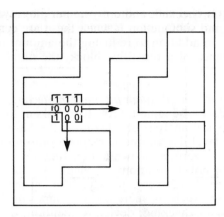

Fig. 10.6 Localization of data through windowing.

amount of data required at any one time has been adopted in a hardware dimension rule checker, in which the bit map of a section of the layout is generated where and when it is required.

10.2.2 REDUCTION IN THE NUMBER OF SPURIOUS ERRORS [5]

A source of annoyance to designers is DRC programs which produce large numbers of spurious errors, since time is wasted checking out these false errors, and a true error which has been reported amidst the false ones may be overlooked. The main reason for the high incidence of false errors is that the DRC program operates on a data file which is devoid of any topological or device information which may be used to reduce these errors. For example, a common source of false error is butting shapes, which, although functionally correct, would fail a minimum separation check. This situation may be avoided if the shapes are merged prior to the test; however, this has the disadvantage of producing more complex shapes on which dimension checks have to performed. An alternative solution is to perform a connectivity check first, to establish which shapes may touch and thus isolate any unintentional short circuits before a dimension rule check is performed. Another source of spurious error results from using 'shape based' algorithms, where in order to perform a minimum separation check one shape is inflated by the minimum separation distance, and a check is made for overlap with another shape; this construction, however, increases the size of the shape at the corners by an amount greater than the minimum separation distance, which can result in shapes which conform to the design rule being reported as violating the minimum separation rule. Some spurious errors may be avoided by retaining some knowledge of the function of a given shape. For example, if a resistor is realized using a meander structure, as shown in Fig. 10.7a, the inter-limb spacing rule must not be violated, since a short circuit would alter the resistance value; however, the inter-limb spacing violation on a mask identifier, shown in Fig. 10.7b, is of little importance. With respect to the polysilicon gate process, another source of spurious error is flagging butting contacts as undersized transistors. In this particular case spurious errors can be avoided if

139 / Topological analysis tools

commonly used groups of shapes are represented by 'symbols' in the layout; it is then sufficient to check one instance of the 'symbol' for design rule violations.

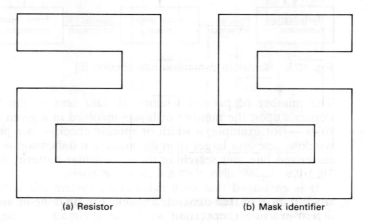

    (a) Resistor   (b) Mask identifier

Fig. 10.7 Dimension rule pathologies.

In addition to spurious errors being reported certain design rules are omitted: for example, the width of conductors is checked for minimum dimensions but the width is never checked against its required current-carrying capacity; this type of design rule is circuit dependent.

10.2.3 A HARDWARE DIMENSION RULE CHECKER [6]

In addition to introducing special purpose hardware for simulation, attempts have been made to design a hardware dimension rule checker, which will perform width checks, edge connection checks and Boolean mask operations. The hardware is used to do the repetitive tasks, which can be done quickly, whilst the software performs all the irregular functions.

A simple block diagram of the system is shown in Fig. 10.8. Initially the layout is rasterized into a grid of square cells, each mask level being represented by a bit in each cell. However, unlike most raster scan techniques the layout is not stored as a bit map, but is generated line by line by the system software as required.

The checks performed by the hardware are

(1)   width checks;
(2)   separation checks;
(3)   inflate and deflate operations;
(4)   overlap and enclosure checks;
(5)   Boolean operations on mask.

The way in which the hardware performs a dimension check is as follows. First an active line is loaded into the rasterizing hardware where a bit map of the line is produced. The parallel streams of rasterized data are subsequently passed to the 'local area' hardware which performs window pattern checks.

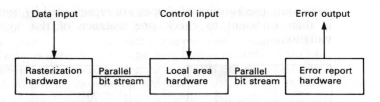

Fig. 10.8 Hardware dimension rule checker.[6]

The number of parallel streams of data sent to the 'local area' hardware depends upon the number of layers involved in a given check. Specific design rules — for example, a width or spacing check — are performed by passing a window, one unit larger than the minimum dimension being checked, over the rasterized line and searching for a particular pattern, as discussed in Section 10.2.1.

It is envisaged that such a hardware system might be incorporated into a work station so that dimension checks can be done immediately rather than as a post-processing operation.

10.3 Mask layout to function verification [7]

After the layout of a circuit has been designed a major issue which requires to be resolved is whether or not the layout realizes the intended circuit function. In the past this verification procedure was carried out manually by tracing through the circuit identifying load devices, thereafter analysing the configuration of the associated pull-down devices to establish the logic function of the gate and then establishing the interconnectivity of the gates; this process is an extremely arduous task when it is used on complex circuits. Consequently layout to function verification programs were developed which were not only more efficient with respect to time, but also more reliable in detecting errors in the layout.

A layout to function verification program comprises four sub-programs to

(1) locate active devices;
(2) synthesize active devices into logic functions;
(3) establish interconnectivity between functions;
(4) compare the reconstructed circuit with a reference circuit.

Ideally, the program should be independent of technology, be able to deal with arbitrary shapes and not require any additional mask data, in the form of labels, to be supplied by the designer.

10.3.1 LOCATION OF ACTIVE DEVICES [8]

The location of devices in a layout relies heavily on a set of routines which perform topological checks on the layout, such as checking for overlaps, enclosure or abutment. For example, in the silicon gate technology the location of transistors is a relatively trivial task, since a device is located in a region where there is an overlap between the polysilicon and diffusion well; care, however, must be exercised to eliminate butting contacts which are also located at regions where polysilicon and diffusion overlap. Contacts and transistors can be differentiated by comparing the size of the overlap regions with the design rule for a minimum-sized transistor, the overlap region of the butting contact being less than the length of such a transistor. The bit-map technique is a very efficient method for identifying polysilicon gate transistors, since it involves simply ANDing the polysilicon and diffusion mask levels. Enhancement and depletion mode devices can also be distinguished by ANDing the active device area with the ion-implantation mask.

If the device recognition program is to be technology independent it does require a data file which defines the construction of the devices in terms of the mask levels involved and their relationship, together with some qualifying statements to distinguish it from other components which use the same mask levels but in a different topological relationship, such as transistors and butting contacts.

10.3.2 SYNTHESIS OF GATE FUNCTIONS [9]

The synthesis of a gate function is essentially the problem of establishing local interconnectivity between individual devices, and comprises searching out a d.c. path from power to ground lines. If, after the load device is located, a single series path is traced through the pull-down devices, the gate will perform the NAND function; however, if there are several paths each containing only one transistor, the gate will perform the NOR function. If the parallel paths contain more than one transistor the gate will perform the AND–OR–INVERT function. The synthesis of a CMOS gate is more complex, however, and starts at the output node of the gate. Paths are then traced to the appropriate power lines, and if a series chain of devices is found in the p-well a parallel set of devices must be present in the n-well and vice versa. However, if the gate realizes a Boolean expression, as shown in Fig. 10.9, it is necessary to resort to graph theory to establish the function and to ensure that the dual of the function is realized in the p- and n-wells.

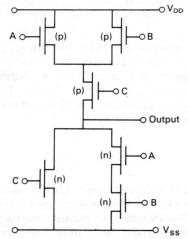

Fig. 10.9 CMOS complex gate.

10.3.3 ESTABLISHMENT OF INTERCONNECTIVITY [10]

In some situations this can be a relatively simple task, particularly if the layout is generated using a cell library, since it is then only necessary to locate the polygons on various layers which connect the library blocks together. If the routing between the blocks is done automatically and the interconnection nets derived directly from a logic description of the system, the connectivity check is redundant.

In general, however, establishing the circuit connectivity entails locating the output node of a structure and tracing a path from that node to the input node of some other structure. In tracing the path between the source and sink nodes it is necessary to ascend and descend layers in the layout via contact cuts.

10.3.4 COMPARISON WITH REFERENCE CIRCUIT [11]

The comparison of the reconstructed circuit with the reference circuit is a difficult problem, and three techniques have been used:

(1) connectivity comparison at circuit level;
(2) connectivity comparison at logic level;
(3) simulation at switch level.

The connectivity comparison performed at circuit level is too detailed for large circuits and is used only on basic cells. The comparison at gate level permits larger functions to be checked, but requires the recognition of gate structures, which can be a difficult problem in MOS since in some instances there is no one-to-one correspondence with a logic function and its physical realization. Consequently, this level of comparison can be used effectively only if the designer is constrained to using specific gate types. The comparison between the reconstructed circuit and the reference circuit using switch level simulation has several advantages in that no reference connectivity is required and no constraints are imposed upon the designer regarding gate types. It has the disadvantage, however, that if the simulation results show an error in the circuit, it is difficult to locate the error since the fault resolution of this technique is minimal.

The problem of comparing the circuit derived from layout with the intended function can be eased to some extent by placing labels in the layout which correspond to gate nodes in the logic diagram, and this procedure localizes the connectivity check. However, labelling the layout can be a tedious process and consequently errors can occur. An alternative to the comparative methods described is to resort to graph theory [12] to check that the graph of the derived circuit is isomorphic with that of the reference circuit.

10.4 Electrical design rule checking and parameter extraction [13]

The performance of a MOS circuit is dependent upon its topology and as device dimensions are reduced the current driving capability of the device is reduced, consequently their ability to charge and discharge the circuit capacitances is also reduced. Thus, when determining the response of a circuit, it is essential to account for all parasitic capacitances and resistances so that their effect may be evaluated during circuit simulation.

The analysis of the parasitic components is performed by electrical design rule checking and parametric extraction programs which rely on information generated by the dimension checking and layout to function verification programs: for example, areas of shapes (calculation of capacitance and transistor aspect ratios), separation distances between shapes (calculation of coupling capacitance) connectivity nets (calculation of resistance and capacitance) etc.

10.4.1 CALCULATION OF CAPACITANCES [14]

The physical construction of an integrated circuit implicitly creates large numbers of capacitors in the layout, as shown in Fig. 10.10, which must be

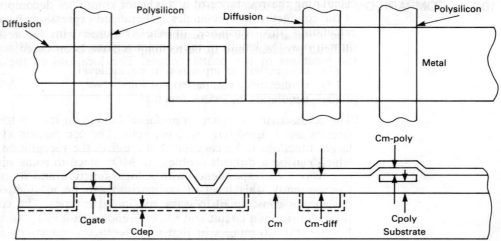

Fig. 10.10 Parasitic layout capacitances. Cgate — polysilicon to channel capacitance. Cdep — diffusion to substrate capacitance. Cm — metal to substrate capacitance. Cm-diff — metal to diffusion capacitance. Cm-poly — metal to polysilicon capacitance. Cpoly — polysilicon to substrate capacitance.

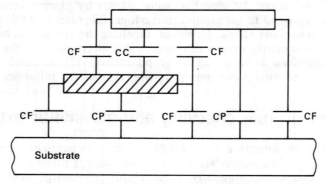

Fig. 10.11 Inter-conductor capacitances. CF — fringing capacitance, CC — coupling capacitance. CP — parallel plate capacitance.

accounted for when determining the capacitance that given device must charge or discharge; these are essentially parallel plate capacitors, and actual values of capacitance per unit area are supplied by the manufacturer for a given process. Other capacitors which must be accounted for, shown in Fig. 10.11, are fringe and coupling capacitances between substrate and other conductors. Several circuit extraction programs have been developed to calculate these values automatically from the layout.

10.4.2 CALCULATION OF RESISTANCE [15]

The calculation of the resistance of various conductors in the circuit is much more difficult than the capacitance calculations, which are obtained by determining the values for areas involved in producing a given capacitor and multiplying by the appropriate value for that process. The basic technique for calculating the resistance of a conductor comprises decomposing the geometry of the conductor into rectangles; generalized expressions have been derived for calculating the resistance of the rectangles in terms of their physical dimensions, the length of the contact regions between adjacent rectangles and the locations of the contact edges. The locations of the contact edges are

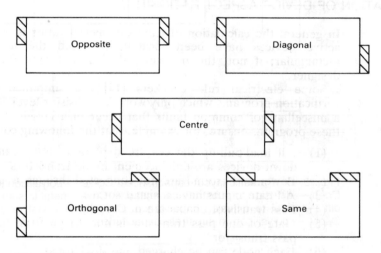

Fig. 10.12   Contact classifications.[15]

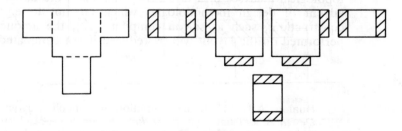

Fig. 10.13   Fracturing of a polygon to calculate its resistance.

145 / Topological analysis tools

grouped into five categories, as shown in Fig. 10.12: opposite, diagonal, centre, orthogonal and on the same side. Branch points in a conductor generate rectangles which have one input port and two output ports, as shown in Fig. 10.13. In this instance, each output in turn is blocked off whilst a path is traced through the remaining output. By this technique the fractured conductor is converted into a resistance network, as shown in Fig. 10.14, and the resistance between the nodes can be calculated.

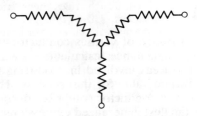

Fig. 10.14   Resistor network derived from fractured polygon.

10.4.3   CALCULATION OF DEVICE ASPECT RATIOS [16]

In general the calculation of transistor aspect ratios is a trivial task once the active devices have been located, provided the active device area is rectangular; if not, the particular device is flagged for verification by the designer.

Some electrical rule checkers [17] are simplified layout to function verification programs which only work at transistor level and are used to locate a miscellany of common faults that occur in a layout. Checks performed by these programs ensure, for example, that the following conditions are satisfied.

(1)   All load/pull-up devices are depletion mode transistors, and all pull down devices are enhancement mode transistors.
(2)   Power and ground are not connected through a single transistor.
(3)   All gate inputs have a signal source.
(4)   Pass transistor chains are not too long.
(5)   Gate of one pass transistor is not driven from the output of another pass transistor.
(6)   Each node can be charged and discharged.

However, as remarked at the beginning of this chapter, the need to perform topological analyses of a layout depends upon the design style, and with the advent of design methodologies which attempt to ensure 'correctness by construction', such as silicon compilers [18], the amount of analysis to be performed on the layout will be reduced if not eliminated completely.

References

1.   Dunlop, A.E. SLIM: the translation of Symbolic Layout Into Mask data. *17th Design Automation Conference Proceedings*, 595–602 (1980).
2.   Wilmore, J.A. Efficient Boolean operations on IC masks. *18th Design Automation Conference Proceedings*, 571–9 (1981).

3. Wilmore, J.A. A hierarchical bit-map format for the representation of mask data. *17th Design Automation Conference Proceedings*, 585–90 (1980).

4. Dobes, I. and Byrd, R. The automatic recognition of silicon gate transistor geometries — an LSI design aid program. *13th Design Automation Conference Proceedings*, 327–35 (1976).

5. McGrath, E.J. and Whitney, T. Design integrity and immunity checking: a new look at layout verification and design rule checking. *17th Design Automation Conference Proceedings*, 263–8 (1980).

6. Seiler, L. A hardware assisted design rule check architecture. *19th Design Automation Conference Proceedings*, 232–8 (1982).

7. Baird, H.S. and Cho, Y.E. An artwork design verification system. *12th Design Automation Conference Proceedings*, 414–20 (1975).

8. Szantol, L. Network recognition of an MOS integrated circuit from the topography of its masks. *Computer Aided Design*, **10**(2), 135–40 (1978).

9. Takashima, M. *et al.* Programs for verifying circuit connectivity of MOS/LSI mask artwork. *19th Design Automation Conference Proceedings*, 544–50 (1982).

10. Mitsuhashi, T., *et al.* An integrated mask artwork analysis program. *17th Design Automation Conference Proceedings*, 277–84 (1980).

11. Ablasser, I. and Jager, U. Circuit recognition and verification based on layout information. *18th Design Automation Conference Proceedings*, 684–9 (1981).

12. Watanabe, T. *et al.* A new automatic logic interconnection verification system for VLSI design. *IEEE Trans. Computer Aided Design of Integrated Circuits and Systems*, **CAD-2**(2), 70–81 (1983).

13. Losleben, P. and Thompson, K. Topological analysis for VLSI circuits. *16th Design Automation Conference Proceedings*, 461–73 (1979).

14. Tarolli, G.M. and Herman, W.J. Hierarchical circuit extraction with detailed parasitic capacitance. *20th Design Automation Conference Proceedings*, 337–45 (1983).

15. Bastian, J.D. *et al.* Symbolic parasitic extractor for circuit simulation (SPECS). *20th Design Automation Conference Proceedings*, 346–52 (1983).

16. Sakawyke, G., *et al.* A set of programs for MOS design. *18th Design Automation Conference Proceedings*, 435–42 (1981).

17. Corbin, L.V. Custom VLSI electrical rule checking in an intelligent terminal. *18th Design Automation Conference Proceedings*, 696–791 (1981).

18. Mostow, J. A decision based framework for understanding hardware compilers. *Proc. VLSI and Software Engineering Workshop*, 117–25 (1982).

11 Partitioning, placement and automatic layout

11.1 Introduction

Automation of the layout of an integrated circuit is usually divided into a series of sequential tasks, as follows.

(1) Partitioning of a very large system into smaller subunits which may be realized as chips, or be part of a single large chip.
(2) Placement of the subunits on a chip into absolute or relative locations to minimize the overall area and ensure that the final stage of finding the interconnections is possible.
(3) Routing of the actual interconnections.

The reason for this division is to reduce a very difficult problem into a set of simpler subtasks, but there are design tools which combine placement and routing, or other parts of the problem, and there are good reasons for doing so provided the computational task does not become intractable.

Partitioning a VLSI system is no different in essentials from designing any other large system since in taking it from the specification to realisation, the design must be divided down into the sub-units, and these further subdivided until known realizable objects are reached. This decomposition process is best done from the top down, starting from a clear statement of the required function of the final product.

11.2 Partitioning

There is no clear way of measuring the effectiveness of a given partition of any system, and presently no algorithm which can be used to decompose a design into the optimum set of sub-units, but there are a number of objectives to the process, against which a particular partition can be assessed. Some of the more important of these are described below.

11.2.1 REGULARITY

It is obvious that economies can be made if a design can be implemented by connecting together a number of identical chips rather that the same number of different chips, and this is partly an illustration of the fact that the total complexity of the problem and hence the design time has been reduced by a partition which reduces the number of different kinds of sub-units. The design time required to put the sub-units together will also be lowered if there are fewer kinds of sub-unit and these economies apply both to sub-units made as separate chips as well as to partitioning within the chip.

A good measure of this reduction in complexity is the *regularity* of the design (the ratio of total design area to individually crafted parts of the design); for example, a memory chip in which there are many identical instances of a single kind of memory cell is very regular.

11.2.2 NUMBER OF INTERCONNECTIONS

The number of connections between sub-units in a partition is also related to its complexity, and hence design difficulties may increase because of this in an inappropriate partition. More importantly the cost and performance of an integrated circuit are adversely affected if it needs a large number of connections to the outside world, and similarly partitions internal to the chip affect the chip performance more as the technology progresses and more of the levels of the design hierarchy are absorbed onto the chip.

There is an observed partitioning relationship known as Rent's rule, whereby the average terminal count, T, in a network of interconnected blocks of gates, is related to the block count, C, and two constants A and P by the expression.

$$T = AC^P$$

Taking this as a starting point Donath and Mikhail [1] have calculated the size of wiring channels required to interconnect a series of gate arrays of different sizes and aspect ratios, and compared the results to measurements in a study at IBM, which shows that calculations based on Rent's rule provide a useful guide to the wiring channels needed in a ULA.

Typically the average length of wires in a square gate array is given by

$$R = \frac{4}{3}\left[\left(\frac{M^{P-0.5}-1}{4^{P-0.5}-1}\right) - \left(\frac{1-M^{P-1.5}}{1-4^{P-1.5}}\right)\right]$$

where R is measured in gate pitches and M is the number of gates in the array.

Table 11.1 shows extensions of this work to non-square arrays, where the importance is that it allows calculation of the wiring channel size for a ULA.

If wide enough channels are provided in a ULA there will be little difficulty in routing with a *simple* algorithm. Whilst 100% routing is essential for a ULA, it cannot always be obtained even with very sophisticated techniques and large amounts of computation.

Given a bit more room, complete layout can often be achieved with a very simple layout algorithm and little computation time.

Table 11.2 gives a comparison between the number of x and y tracks

Table 11.1 Average connection length (measured in gate pitches)

Array configuration (rows × columns)	Experimental results	Theoretical results
10 × 68	4.39	4.0
14 × 49	3.67	3.41
18 × 38	3.37	3.16
26 × 26	3.07	2.87
38 × 18	3.19	3.16
49 × 14	3.44	3.41
68 × 10	3.99	4.0

Table 11.2 Wiring results

Experimental					Theoretical		
Array configuration	Total number of tracks per gate	T^x	T^y	Observed number of overflows	Total number of tracks per gate	T^x	T^y
		14	6	49			
		13	7	25			
10 × 68	20	12	8	12	19.6	13.9	5.7
		11	9	27			
		10	10	47			
		10	8	25			
14 × 49	17	9	9	24	17.8	11.1	6.7
		8	10	40			
		9	8	27			
18 × 38	17	8	9	20	17.1	9.7	7.4
		7	10	32			
		9	7	63			
		8	8	27			
26 × 26	16	7	9	24	16.4	8.2	8.2
		6	10	58			
		7	10	27			
38 × 18	17	6	11	25	17.1	7.4	9.7
		5	12	39			
		6	12	34			
48 × 14	18	5	13	32	17.8	6.8	11.1
		4	14	39			
		7	12	72			
		6	13	28			
68 × 10		5	14	22	19.6	5.7	13.9
		3	15	63			
		3	16	133			

T^x = number of x tracks provided
T^y = number of y tracks provided

required by theory and the results in routing actual arrays, indicating as overflows the number of connections that failed.

11.3   Placement methods

The main aim of the placement algorithm in ULA and other semi-custom structures is to provide the basis for the following routing process. Usually, the wiring channel space allocated between rows and columns of gates is a compromise between economy in the use of silicon and the space needed to give a high probability of successful layout, but because any electrically valid design can be entered it may not be possible to route all the connections even if the placement is good, and in general it is difficult to estimate simply how good a given placement is until the actual routing has been done.

The computation required to investigate all possible placements is prohibitive because the number of different placements is proportional to $n!$, where n is the number of components to be placed. Many methods attempt to estimate the 'goodness' of partial placements as the process progresses, choosing only the 'best' module to place next in the 'best' location. This involves continually estimating the 'cost' of selecting a module and placing it in a particular location. The process of cost estimation must be fast in order to explore as many placement variations as possible, but must also bear as close a relation to the actual routing process as possible to be realistic.

A typical method for placement is as follows:

(1)   Generate a new good initial solution.
(2)   Improve the solution by local optimization.
(3)   If the available computation time has not been exhausted then go to Step 1, otherwise choose the best solution amongst those already generated.

11.3.1   INITIAL PLACEMENT

The initial solutions are produced by an algorithm which simply constructs the result starting from a seed, [2] proceeding as follows:

(1)   Decide on the unplaced module most heavily connected to those already placed.
(2)   Place the module selected on a unfilled position so as to give the minimum projected cost (wire length).

An element of randomness can be introduced into the selection in Step 1 to ensure that new solutions are produced each time the algorithm is called, and the starting point (the seed) may be either the pin connections for the chip, or a module selected by some other criterion and placed in the centre of the chip.

11.3.2   FORCE DIRECTED RELAXATION

A simple method of local optimization is to select the most heavily connected pair of modules and attempt a trial interchange. If the wire length improves as

151 / Partitioning, placement and automatic layout

a result, the change is confirmed. A generalization of this [3] might interchange more than two modules at a time, moving A to B, B to C and C back to A's position, for example, and the number of modules involved in the interchange is said to be λ.

If a module is initially placed a long distance from a potential interchange position, it is unlikely that the change will be worth the computation involved. Only a limited set, ε, of positions is usually investigated, being those entailing the shortest estimated wire lengths for the module in consideration.

In Fig. 11.1 the goodness of a particular placement is measured by the total wire length in the subsequent routing, and the computation time as a function of the parameters ε and λ is shown.

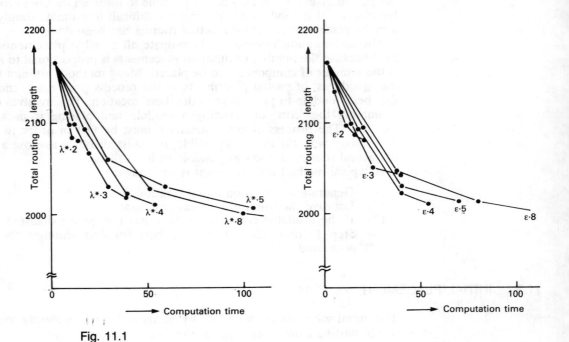

Fig. 11.1

Estimates of goodness by wire length provide a guide to placement improvement; unfortunately they also tend to bunch components in a relatively small area, leading to difficulties of congestion in the wiring channels in that area, and Figs 11.2 and 11.3 show the connection paths found for a design placed manually in Fig. 11.2, and placed by an algorithm which attempts to minimize wire length in Fig. 11.3. These clearly indicate a bunching of components in the top right-hand corner of the automatically placed chip, which caused failure of connections to route (the numbered squares indicate the failed connection points).

It is clearly better to attempt to minimize the congestion in the wiring channels rather than the wire length itself, and many systems now do this, using weighting functions which depend on the probability of a wire using a particular channel and the likely occupancy of that channel by the other wires.

152 / CAD for VLSI

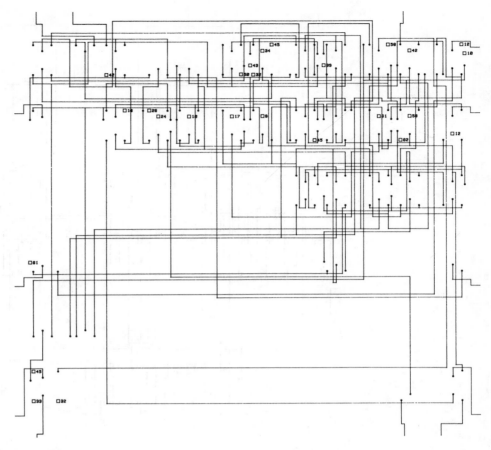

Fig. 11.2

11.3.3 MIN-CUT PLACEMENT

Rather than simply placing re-existing modules, some methods attempt to partition the network in a rational way, and the Mincut algorithm [4] is one such. Modules are placed to the left or right of a cut line parallel to the y axis in such a way as to reduce the number of connections crossing the line to a minimum, with the difference in area between the two halves not exceeding a certain threshold. The partitions are themselves cut parallel to the x axis and the process repeated recursively. The development is illustrated in Fig. 11.4, in which a graphical representation of the design shows the modules as arcs in the graph and the channel between as nodes. Since the partitioning reduces the number of connections between modules, routing problems should be eased.

There are many other initial placement methods, but whilst adequate results are now being produced they are often inferior to the human designer in some situations and particularly where there is an easily identifiable structure to the design.

153 / Partitioning, placement and automatic layout

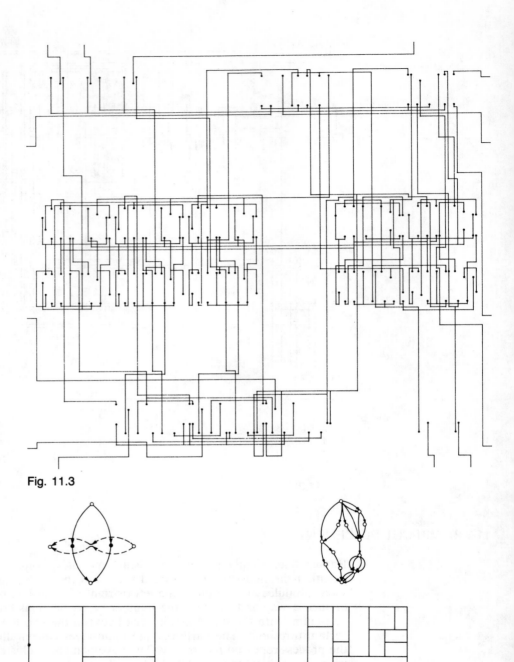

Fig. 11.3

Fig. 11.4

154 / CAD for VLSI

11.3.4 DESIGN STRUCTURE

The kind of structure which placement algorithms are not able to identify easily is one which can make use of the two-dimensional properties of the chip.

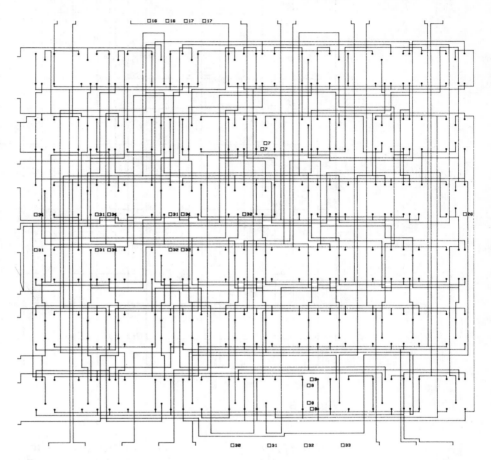

Fig. 11.5

Fig. 11.5 shows the connections produced by an autorouter for a hand-placed array of 12 × 12 gates arranged on a 144 cell ULA. In this example the connections are a single *X–Y* arrangement such as might be found in a RAM or decoder, but since each gate is equally interconnected to every other gate on its row or column it is not possible for automatic placement algorithms to make a choice easily of which of the unconnected gates to take next, and the choice of location for that module cannot just be made on wire length if the best layout is to be found.

Clearly the structure inherent in the design has been ignored by the placement algorithm and the penalty for this can be clearly seen in the difference between the auto-placed and the hand-placed arrays in Figs. 11.5 and 11.6.

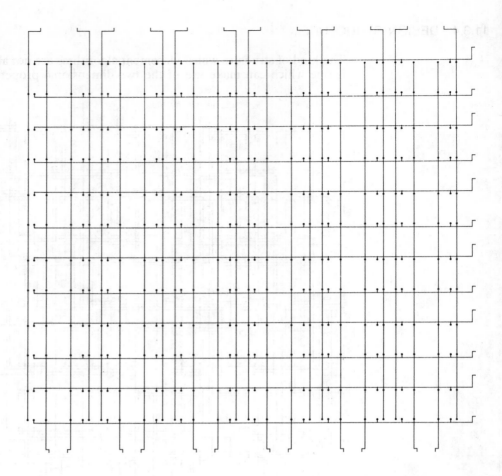

Fig. 11.6

One approach to improvement of placement is the 'brute force' method of increasing the computational resources to explore more and more placement possibilities more accurately, but this is a method likely to prove very costly as the number of gates on a chip increases.

Most design automation systems therefore combine the accuracy and analysis of a relatively simple algorithm with interaction by the designer to provide the insights necessary to explore any structure in the design.

11.4 Routing

After placement of components, the routing software must determine the precise paths of the interconnections between connection points. Again this is a problem in which the very large number of connections required interact with each other in a way which makes the exploration of all possible paths impractical for chips of present complexity, and algorithms have to be found which can provide a solution without overflow tracks for a ULA, or within an acceptable area for cell-based technologies.

The problem of routing, can itself by split up into simpler problems and one of the tasks is to find the connection path for each set of connected points in turn. The sets of points which are to be electrically connected are termed nets, and the first step is to form a list of nets ordered in a way intended to make the overall routing process likely to be successful. Each net is then taken in turn and the detailed paths between the connection points found.

At the simplest level there are several algorithms and heuristics which have been used to join a net of points.

11.4.1 THE LEE PATH CONNECTION ALGORITHM

Perhaps the most commonly used method for finding the shortest path between two points was described by Lee in 1961. [5]

In essence this consists of choosing one point as the source, S and the other as the target, T. The area to be explored to find the path is divided into a grid of cells each of unit size, and is represented by a data structure such as an array. The source cell in the array is then marked with an integer. The address of this marked cell is then placed into a list called the frontier cell list, and all unmarked neighbours of the frontier cells are then marked with the next integer. When no more unmarked neighbours exist, the old frontier cell list is deleted and replaced by the list of newly marked cells. The process is then repeated as shown in Fig. 11.7 until the target cell is hit.

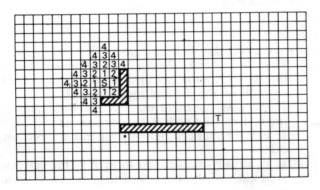

Fig. 11.7

If the frontier cell list has no members at any point before the target is reached, there can be no path between the source and target. Lee's algorithm thus guarantees that if a path exists it will be found, and that the path found will be the shortest, since at any time the minimum path length to every frontier cell is equal.

The actual path can easily be retraced by following back from the target to the source looking at each point for the previous integer in the sequence.

The reason for the ubiquity of Lee's algorithm is its adaptability. It can easily cope with multipoint nets by expanding from all points simultaneously and retracing in both directions from a contact point, and can also be modified to deal with multilayer metal by using a three-dimensional array structure to represent the grid rather than the two-dimensional structure of Fig. 11.7.

A modification of Lee's algorithm has been described by Rubin [6] in which the cost of expanding a particular cell can be made a function of the direction of expansion (less for movement towards the target, more for movement away). Where a large number of possible cells with the same cost could be expanded, Rubin proposed that the latest cell added to the cell list be expanded. Such an algorithm is known as a 'depth first predictor'.

The actual algorithm is as follows: its action is illustrated in Fig. 11.8.

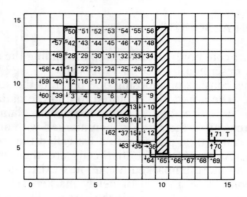

Fig. 11.8 Mark map.

(1) Set a cost threshold to zero.
(2) Find the last cell, 'c', in a cell list whose estimated cost equals the cost threshold. If none, set the cost threshold to the least estimated cost of any cell on the list and repeat Step 2.
(3) If the cost threshold exceeds the maximum allowable cost for this track, Exit (the path is too expensive).
(4) If 'c' is a target cell, note its expansion direction in a 'mark' array and exit.
(5) If 'c' already marked, go to Step 8 (the cell has been expanded).
(6) Add each of the unmarked neighbours of 'c' to a cell list with their cost.
(7) Note the expansion direction of 'c' in the 'mark' array.
(8) Delete 'c' from the cell list.
(9) If the cell list is empty, exit (no path exists).
(10) Go to Step 2.

The cost of a neighbour cell in Fig. 11.8 is the sum of its distance from the prime target and a fixed expansion cost of one unit per move. Since the latest minimum cost cell is always the one expanded, expansion takes place preferentially towards the target.

This algorithm can also be modified to favour the X direction on one layer, and the Y direction on the order, as well as adding penalties for other obstacles, such as vias.

11.4.2 HEURISTICS

Cellular routers such as Lee's algorithm may explore very large areas of board before a successful connection is found, and since the area is explored on a cell-by-cell basis the computation required is considerble. If the number of connections is proportional to the number of gates n, and the average length proportional to $n^{\frac{1}{2}}$, the area explored per connection is at least proportional to n in a simple Lee router and the total layout time at least proportional to n^2.

This may be worse if the connections are difficult to find and most of the chip area has to be explored to find the connections.

Usually, however, about 75% of connections are relatively simple, involving nothing more than a straight connection, or one with at most one or two bends. A heuristic approach which attempts to find these simple connections quickly by extending parallel lines from the two points and connection between the lines with an orthogonal line was first described by Aramaki *et al.* [7] in 1971; and has the advantage of following an *x-y* path which, as well as being quick to compute, is less likely to block subsequent nets than the more complex paths sometimes produced by Lee's algorithm. Fig. 11.9 shows the kind of paths found by a simple heuristic using two layouts of interconnect, and in Fig. 11.10 a section of the layout of a 2000-gate CMOS ULA shows its use in conjunction with a final pass using Lee's algorithm.

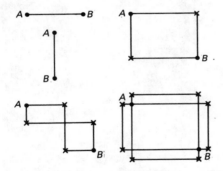

Fig. 11.9 Possible routes with two or fewer bends.

11.4.3 NET INFORMATION

Splitting a multi-point net into pairs of points allows the actual paths between the points to be found either by a heuristic or by a variant of Lee's algorithm. In practice, however, the total wire length produced depends upon the order in which points are joined to the main body of the net, as well as the general form of the tree joining all the points.

The configuration giving the minimum wire length is known as a Steiner tree, but unfortunately the computation required to produce this in the general case is intractable [8] and simple methods often give adequate results. A typical algorithm would first connect the two nearest points on the net, then join each next nearest point to the tree already formed.

If a cell-based connection algorithm is used, it is possible to expand each point in the net simultaneously until all expansions touch each other.

159 / Partitioning, placement and automatic layout

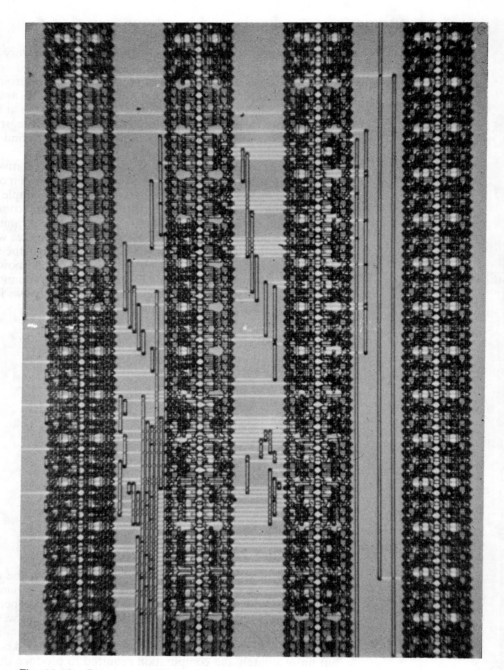

Fig. 11.10 Gate array wiring.

11.5 Channel routers

One disadvantage of grid-based routes is the amount of memory required to store the data structure. Arrays of over 100 000 elements are commonly required and will increase with the scale of integration.

Rather than looking at each net in turn and dividing the area available into a grid of cells, many recent routers examine each row or column in order to pack connections optimally in the wiring channel formed between the rows or columns. An early method was described by Hashimoto and Stevens. [9] Here all the nets participating in the use of a particular channel are considered at the same time, and the aim is to minimize the channel width required to provide the connections and through routes. Another advantage is that the connections are stored as wire segments with start and end points only, using much less memory than the cells of grid routers, and usually faster in testing whether or not a segment exists at a particular position.

To find a routing giving a minimal area or minimal wire length within a channel is in general a difficult problem, and solutions usually attempt to find a solution only in channel widths, close to the optimum with reasonable computation time.

A fairly complex situation is Fig. 11.11, where it can be seen that the layout cannot be completed with a single horizontal connection for each of the nets numbered 1 to 9. This is because conflicts exist between the nets — for example between net 5 and net 9 which require the horizontal segment of net 5 to be above that of net 9 on the left, but below on the right. Resolution of these conflicts forces the insertion of an extra 'dog leg' horizontal and vertical section which may require the channel to be expanded.

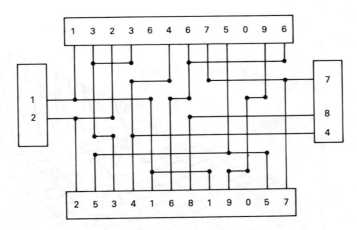

Fig. 11.11 A routing of nine nets (width = 7).

An algorithm which can be used to achieve an adequate final routing is as follows:

(1) Determine the constraints which must exist at each point along the channel (i.e. which horizontal segment must be above which).

(2) Assign a vertical order to the horizontal segments at each point which

conforms to the constraints, and fits closest with the order in the previous and following points.

(3) If necessary, introduce dog legs between successive points to accommodate the reordering.

A further rearrangement step may also be incorporated at the end to optimize the total area by moving segments up or down without changing the order.

11.6 Hierarchical routing

In a completely global router which tackles the whole routing problem in one pass using a net routing algorithm such as Lee's algorithm, the amount of computation required is at least proportional to the square of the number of gates. Considerable savings in time can be made by the use of local channel routers which consider the detailed wiring of a relatively small area in a big chip without regard to the surrounding area. If each small area is considered in turn, the computation is clearly not much greater than proportional to the number of gates, but there is a need for an earlier, global planning stage to assign nets to channels before the detailed routing is done, and there may be the possibility of backtracking to the global stage again if a particular channel proves impossible with the initial allocation of wires.

In a global router, the chances of a connection going through a particular channel are estimated, the probable number of connections calculated for each channel and compared with the channel capacity by using an empirically derived cost function such as that shown in Fig. 11.12.

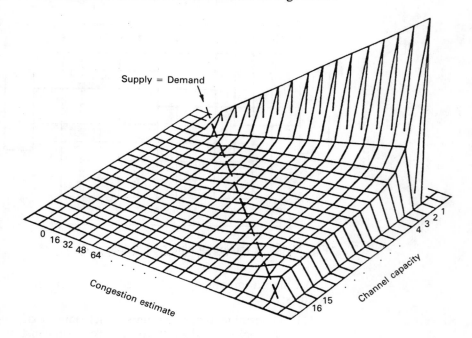

Fig. 11.12

The cost of routing the wires along a particular path can now be estimated, and the global router tries to decide which channel to actually use in order to minimize the cost.

There are two areas where further improvements in computing time and economy of memory can be made within this scenario: these are

(1) The use of pre-wired macros. The greater the regularity factor in the design the greater advantage can be taken of laying out a block of gates once and copying that block in the positions required, rather than computing in detail every part of the chip area.

(2) Greater use of hierarchy. There is no reason to stop at two levels in the hierarchy of the design (global and local), and some advantage may be gained from matching the layout hierarchy to the conceptual hierarchy in the input text provided by the designer. This input should also be aimed at regularity and reduction of the number of connections

```
LD
  M=3,7/4;
P=1;
  D=2
CD
  b0(200,100)
    [x1(10,P);x2(50,D);x1(70,P),ignd(150,M)]        {N.249
    [x3(50,D);x4(30,D)]                             {E}
    [vdd(20,M);x1(150,P)]                           {S}
    □              {W}
ICD
  B1(30,40)
    [x5(10,P)]
    [vdd(10,M);x2(20,D);x6(30,P)]
    [x7(10,D)]
    [x8(10D);gnd(20.M);x10(30,P)];
  b2(50,10)
    [gnd(10,M);x2(30,D);x9(40,M)]
    [x1(5,P)]
    [vdd(5,M)]
    [x1(5,P)];
  b3(20,30)
    [x1(10,P)]
    [gnd(5,M);x10(15,D);x4(25,P)]
    [x2(5,M)]
    [vdd(5,M);x5(15,D)]
POS
  >b2/i1.(b1/i1;(−b3/i1.>b3/i1)).b2/i2.(b1/i2;↑ b1/i3)
NET
  □;
  □;
  [//x1,b2//x2];
  [b0//x2,b1/i1/x5,b1/i2/x5,b1//x7];
  [b1/i3/x5,b0//x3/i1/x5];
  [b0//x4,b3/i2/x10,b3//x4,b2//x9];
  [/i1/x10,b1//x8,b1/i1/x6]
END
```

Fig. 11.13 Input describing cell b0 in terms of cells b1, b2 and b3.

between subsystems — both qualities helpful to auto layout — because these aims also reduce the complexity of the design.

An example of the text input for a hierarchical cell-based layout system [10] which employs channel routing is shown in Fig. 11.13, where the blocks to be laid out consist of rectangles with connection points on their boundaries.

Here the name of each component block b_1, b_2 and b_3 to be used is associated with its length and width in brackets, followed by a list of the signal names to be found on the north, east, south and west faces of the block. Each signal name is followed by its distance along the block and the layer used to connect to it (polysilicon, metal or diffusion).

A positional statement after the keyword *POS* describes the relative placement and instantiation of these blocks thus *b1/i1* is instance *i1* of block *b1*. The binary operators . and ; represent the positioning of blocks above or alongside one another, and the unary operators $>$, $\uparrow$, and $-$ represent rotation or mirroring.

Nets are indicated by grouping signals in square brackets, each signal being represented blockname/instance/signal name.

The final result is a higher order block b_0 defined under *CD*, which, after computation to verify or modify the size parameters, can be used as a definition elsewhere.

The global routing process is done with the aid of a channel graph representaton (Fig. 11.14) derived from the text input, and since in this case the layout is not targeted for a ULA with fixed channel widths, the channels can be expanded to accommodate the wire allocated to them. There is now no necessity for overflows, and 100% routing is achievable with the penalty of increased area.

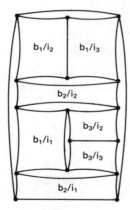

Fig. 11.14   Channel graph induced from the positional expression of Fig. 11.1.

An algorithm related to Lee's algorithm is used to find the optimum global path through the graph and is followed by two successive expansion stages in the y and x directions (Fig. 11.15) where the channel widths actually required are calculated.

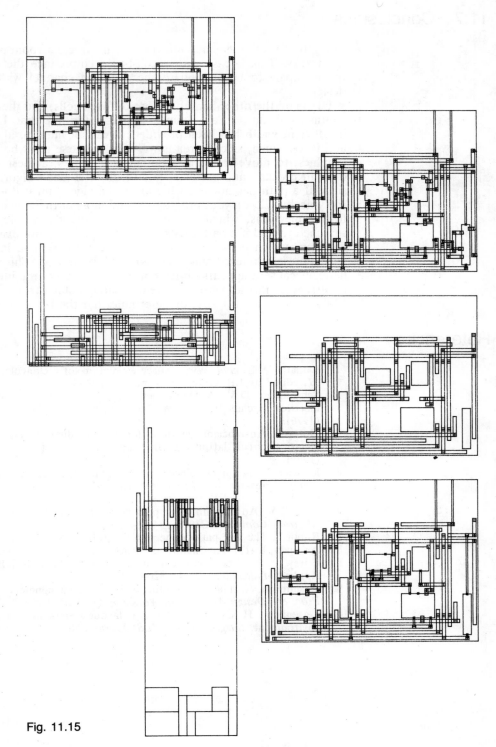

Fig. 11.15

165 / Partitioning, placement and automatic layout

11.7   Conclusions

The job of routing is made much easier if sufficient room is made available for the tracks. This is easy with a cell-based chip, since the cells can always be moved apart to accommodate the required channel widths for a particular design.

ULAs on the other hand have pre-diffused cells, and therefore fixed channel widths constant for all designs implemented on that ULA floor plan. If insufficient width has been provided, it cannot later be altered by the router, and if too much, silicon area is wasted. Recourse must be made to interactive graphics, to move tracks and put in new routes, at best an error prone and difficult process, and particularly difficult after Lee's algorithm has been used, since if a path has not been found by the algorithm it does not exist.

Typically ULA layout programs spend most of their time looking for the last few connections, which are usually long, and the whole chip area must be searched to find if a path exists. Often the paths do not exist because of earlier decisions which prevented access to critical points, and large amounts of the wiring must be altered make the required connection. This is presently done by hand, because it appears difficult at present to make the intelligent judgements necessary in the software at an early enough stage to provide a guarantee of 100% routing for a ULA, or determine that the layout is impossible.

References

1. Donath, W.E. *et al.* Wiring space estimation for rectangular gate arrays. In *VLSI 81*, edited by J.P. Gray, Academic Press (1981).
2. Schweikert, D.V. A two dimensional placement algorithm for the layout of electrical circuits. *Proc. 13th Design Automation Conf.* (San Fransisco) 409–14 (1976).
3. Goto, S. An efficient algorithm for the two dimensional placement problem in electrical circuit layout. *IEEE Trans. Circuits and Systems.* **CAS 28**(1), 12–18 (1981).
4. Lauther, U. A min cut placement algorithm for general cell assemblies based on a graph representation. *Proc. 16th Design Automation Conf.* (San Diego) 1–10 (1979).
5. Lee, C.Y. An algorithm for path connections and its applications. *IRE Trans. Electron. Comput.* **EC10**(3), 346–64 (1961).
6. Rubin F. The Lee path connection algorithm. *IEEE Trans.*, **C23**, 907–14 (1974).
7. Aramaki, I. *et al.* Automation of etching pattern layout. *CACM*, **14**, 720–30 (1971)
8. Garey, M.R. The rectilinear Steiner tree problem is NP-complete. *SIAM J. Applied Mathematics*, **32**(4), 826–34 (1977).
9. Hashimoto, A. *et al.* Wire routing by optimising assignment within large apertures. *Proc. 8th Design Automation Workshop* (Atlantic City), 155–69 (1971).
10. Leisenberg, H.K.E. *et al.* An auto layout system for a hierarchical i.c. design environment. *Integration, the VLSI Journal*, No. 1, 107–19 (1983).

12 High-level languages in design

12.1 Introduction

Integrated circuit design has highlighted the need for a wide range of tools and techniques that may be used to assist the silicon designer. Previous chapters have identified some of them, and a need has been shown for design rule checkers and circuit extractors, automatic routers, and analysis tools such as simulators and timing analysers.

However, the designer may be best assisted by the way in which his design is expressed. If it is inappropriate, then the ability to generate additional information will be severely impaired.

Before the advent of integrated circuits, the traditional form of circuit representation was a diagram. All discussions about and modifications to the design were made to this diagram. Buy any piece of electrical equipment today, and a circuit diagram will be provided along with the owner's handbook, to provide all the information that might be required.

Once small and medium-scale integration became available, a distinct move was made away from the diagramatic representation, primarily because it was not the most suitable form in which to represent the design, particularly when large numbers of changes were to be made.

Instead, designs were represented in a linguistic form. Originally, these languages were very low-level, (e.g. CIF [1]), and were derived directly from the 'languages' which were used to 'program' the hardware used during the fabrication process, such as pattern generators and electron beam machines. The emphasis of such languages was on arranging rectangular shapes, which represented the different mask layers, into patterns which represented the integrated circuit being designed. These languages were machine independent and, by providing suitable conversion programs, a design expressed in such a language could be fabricated using different process routes. Unfortunately, they were an extremely tedious way in which to describe a design and consequently error prone, just as machine code and assembler programming had been. They were slowly replaced by higher-level design languages which used many of the mechanisms of programming languages in order to express the design in as concise and easy to understand a manner as possible. Many of these languages took as a basis a particular programming language, and by using calls to suitable procedures, they generated the required layout information. Language features such as variables, assignment, repetition, procedures and parameters were then directly available to the designer. An example of this approach is the LAP [2] design system, which is based upon the Simula programming language.

However, such languages still only specified and manipulated the IC's actual layout. That is, the manner in which the circuits requested function was implemented at the silicon level. Limited assistance might be provided to ensure that the layout achieved was actually that which correctly implemented the desired function. All the additional checking about the logic of the circuit and its speed had to be done by the designer, either by hand or through other, often independently designed, ancillary tools. Using these tools often involved the designer in specifying yet more additional information (often in a totally new format), and consequently discovering and removing fairly simple design errors could take long periods of time.

What was needed were design languages that were independent of the ultimate layout, and instead allowed the designer to define the behaviour required of a circuit and also (possibly) how that behaviour could be obtained structurally.

> In hardware design, machine specifications are in a constant state of flux, but radical changes to the design are unaffordable if large portions of the design must be redone, as is usually the case if the design consists of geometric primitives. [Silicon] Compilers make changes affordable, giving the designer freedom to explore many design strategies.
>
> David Johansen, *Silicon Compilation*,
> Caltech Ph.D. Thesis, 1981.

Current research is looking towards the design and implementation of such silicon compilers. That is, a software system that, given a high-level description of the function required, and possible clues on how it could be implemented, automatically generates

— suitable geometric primitives
— the electrical characteristics
— timing information
— other appropriate design information

for the integrated circuit that would result. Ideally, nothing further would be necessary from the designer, except to get the chip fabricated. Design changes would be made to the high-level description, whereupon it would be 're-compiled' in order to incorporate those changes.

Unfortunately, the term *silicon compiler* is not well defined, and many types of design tool masquerade under the term. These include PLA and data-path generators, silicon assemblers and layout modelling languages.

The remainder of this chapter will be devoted to briefly describing four high-level design languages, which might also be legitimately termed silicon compilers. They are MODEL, FIRST, ELLA and STRICT.

Production of a completely general purpose silicon compiler is not a trivial design exercise. Many factors must be considered, including the choosing of a syntax, the construction of a syntactic and semantic checking system, the provision of automatic routing and placement tools, and the choosing of suitable analysis tools, such as simulators. Therefore, in some instances, the researchers involved in implementing the language and associated design system may have simplified the design problem by restricting the language or design system in some way. This is particularly true for the languages MODEL and FIRST.

12.2 MODEL

The MODEL language [3] is used as input to the Chipsmith silicon compiler which has been developed by Lattice Logic.

MODEL descriptions will ultimately be implemented as semi-custom integrated circuits using CMOS ULAs. This is in contrast to the other design languages which attempt to support full custom designs. However, the task of designing and writing the compiler, which analyses the MODEL source, is somewhat simpler, as it only needs to produce information necessary to commit the logic array. Part of this information is the list of connections which must be made between the individual components of the array. This is much simpler than producing CIF or another low-level design language.

Descriptions in MODEL are hierarchical. That is, they express the design of the circuit at a number of levels, starting with the entire circuit at the top, and progressing down to the system primitives at the bottom. This approach is true of many design languages. This form of description results from the ideas expressed by the term 'structured programming'[4], which are used extensively by programmers when writing software. This is one of the areas where the problems of the silicon designer have been helped by applying techniques developed for the design of software.

Instead of describing the complete chip, a designer can make use of a comprehensive, parameterized design library, which comes as part of the Chipsmith design system, and will be updated as new parts are added to it. Such libraries might contain basic components such as buffers, registers, pads and counters, or more sophisticated components such as arithmetic logic units.

An intermediate design file is produced by the MODEL compiler from the initial description. This design file may then be used by other design tools. These currently include

(1)   test pattern generators
(2)   functional simulators
(3)   placement and routing tools
(4)   timing analysers
(5)   graphical viewing programs
(6)   electrical characterizers.

Such tools allow feedback about the design to be generated, allowing the designer to make changes, if necessary, to the MODEL description.

To give a flavour of the language to the reader, a short example of it will be given. Anybody with a basic knowledge of a programming language should find no difficulty with the syntax. Fig. 12.1 shows a multiplexer.

The corresponding MODEL description of the multiplexer now follows, and could be used to construct a gate array implementation of the circuit.

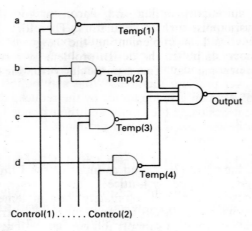

Fig. 12.1 A multiplexer.

```
include "..."
part mux(a,b,c,d,control(1:4)) → output;
   signal temp(1:4)
   nand(a,control(1))   → temp(1)
   nand(b,control(2))   → temp(2)
   nand(c,control(3))   → temp(3)
   nand(d,control(4))   → temp(4)
   nand(temp(1:4))      → output
end  {mux}
inputpad p,q,r,s,select(1:4)
outputpad result
mux(p,q,r,s,select(1:4)) → result
endoffile
```

The notation is easy to read and the resulting descriptions are relatively compact. The **part . . . end** construct (synonomous with a procedure in a programming language) encourages systematic debugging and allows the introduction of suitable abstractions into the design. Parameters highlight the connections to the outside world, and allow the design to be understood independently of it. No facility is provided for hand-wiring; everything must be explicitly stated in the MODEL description. The **inputpad** and **outputpad** statements identify the required connections off the chip, and the final call of the part 'mux' specifies the relation between them and the multiplexer.

Such a description can be manipulated by the design system which is designed to allow a designer to switch from editing a design to compiling it, and so on.

The designer is however responsible for specifying what he wants the circuit to do. This includes providing all the necessary control information, in addition to the data which is to be processed. For large designs this could be a cause of errors in the design, because of the complexities involved. Also as designs become bigger and more complex, they may not actually fit onto particular ULAs (because or limitations in channel size). Such limitations may therefore limit the life of such a design system. Physical debugging of the hardware, though not to be encouraged, will be difficult to achieve, as there will be little indication of which parts of the chip correspond to particular parts of the MODEL description.

However, MODEL and the Chipsmith compiler is available and is being used by customers of Lattice Logic. It has been used to complete successfully semi-custom designs and has proved that such a design system is a definite improvement over previous methods. What may be lost in terms of yield and performance of a circuit is made up for by the reduced design costs in terms of man hours spent designing the circuit and the extended lead time this accrues over competitors who use traditional techniques.

12.3 FIRST: Fast Implementations of Real-time Signal Transforms

FIRST [5] is one of the first fully custom silicon compilers to be designed, and has been implemented by a team at the Department of Electrical and Electronic Engineering at the University of Edinburgh.

FIRST implements systems which are networks of pipelined bit-serial operators. It has been designed expressly to allow rapid investigation and implementation of VLSI digital signal processing systems. Application areas include the design of digital filters and the like.

Unlike the Chipsmith system with its gate array layout, the FIRST compiler is restricted much less in the way it implements the designs presented to it, as would be expected of a fully custom design system. The networks of operators specified in the high-level language description are laid out according to a relatively fixed floorplan. Fig. 12.2 shows a typical FIRST floorplan.

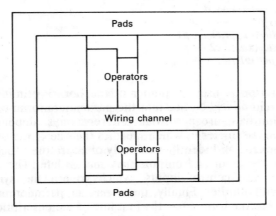

Fig. 12.2   A typical FIRST floorplan.

The operators requested by the designer are implemented as separate function blocks which in turn are constructed from a library of hand-crafted leaf cells. These include cells to multiply, add, subtract, limit, scale, multiplex, sort, bit delay, word delay and handle storage. The function blocks are arranged in two rows, above and below the wiring channel, and are automatically interconnected by the compiler, using information gleaned from the design description. Interconnections between operators are routed through this channel, and the ordering of the operators on each row is determined by the order in which they were specified. Bonding pads are placed around the periphery of the chip, and the order is under the control of the designer.

Input to the compiler is a structural description of the required chip. All the compiler must do is floorplan the elements and perform the necessary routing. Fig. 12.3 shows the flow diagram of an operator used as part of a four-stage cascadable FIR filter section.

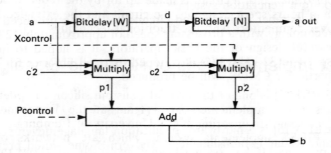

Fig. 12.3 Flow diagram for function *twostage[n]*.

Such a function might be presented to the FIRST compiler using the following high-level description.

operator *TwoStage[n](xctl,pctl)a,c1,c2* → *aout,b*
    signal *d,p1,p2*
    bitdelay[wlth]a → *d*
    bitdelay[n]d   → *aout*
    multiplier(actl)a,c1 → *p1*
    multiplier(xctl)d,c2 → *p2*
    adder(pctl)p1,p2 → *b*
end

This description uses a number of the library primitives, such as *bitdelay*, *multiplier* and *adder*. Notice that the parameters to an operator, including the library primitives, are passed in different ways, depending upon what they signify. The parameter *n*, which specifies the size of the operator, is specified in square brackets, and identifies a family of operators which are different only in the size of the input and outputs they manipulate. The parameters within the parentheses are control inputs, which govern the synchronization of one operator with another. Finally, the remaining parameters, which lie either side of the '→' are the formal (on the first line of the description) and actual (on the remaining lines of the description) input and output names, and specify the interconnections. Local signal names can be declared using the SIGNAL statement.

Similarities will be noticed between the syntax of this description and the previous MODEL description. This is because a large part of the FIRST language compiler is constructed from the similar parts of the MODEL compiler.

Once again, the notation is readable and easy to follow. However, the designer has too much responsibility for placing pads (including power and ground) and for positioning them in the optimal order. At present, tools to carry out this task efficiently are not available, so the engineer must have direct control in order to minimize the amount of wasted silicon and maximize the performance of the resulting chip.

An integrated design environment is provided for the FIRST designer. There is a language compiler, two simulators (one clock driven and the other event driven) and a layout program, and mechanisms exist to convert the output from the simulator to a form which is suitable for use with an automatic test pattern generation system.

A number of integrated circuits have been produced using a 5 μm NMOS technology with a processing speed of approximately 12 kHz. In the future, by careful design of the basic operators, it is hoped to increase the processing speed to 32 kHz. It is also hoped that cell libraries for other technologies, in particular CMOS, will be produced.

12.4 ELLA

ELLA [6] is a hardware specification language developed by the Royal Signal and Radar Establishment at Malvern. Some would prefer to describe it as a hardware description language. It attempts to provide a fully customized integrated circuit design environment. No assumptions are made about how the chip will be laid out structurally.

Associated with the ELLA language is a simulator, database system, incremental compilation facility and other assorted tools.

The language itself is broadly split into two sections. The first is used to describe the functions of certain blocks which are the primitives of the design. The second is used to describe the interconnection of components.

For example, a half adder which adds operands of n bits together might be described in ELLA as follows.

```
type bool = new(t|f|x)                                      #high low unknown#
function HalfAdd =(bool: a b) →
                  (bool, bool):                             #sum carry#
    case (a,b) in (t,t) : (f,t),
                  ((f,t)|(t,f))( : (t,f),
                  (f,f) : (f,f)
        else    (x,x)
    esac
macro NHalfAdd {int n} = ([n] bool: in,bool : cin) →
                         ([n] bool,bool):                   #sum, carryout#
begin
    macro Dummy = ([n] bool: in,bool: cin) →
                  ([n] bool,bool):
    begin
      let one = HalfAdd(in[1],cin),
          rest = NHalfAdd{n−1} (in[2. .n], one[2])
      output (one[1] conc rest[1], rest[2]).
    end
    output if n=1 then
        HalfAdd(in[1],cin)
      else
        Dummy(in,cin)
      fi
end
export: NHalfAdd
finish
```

The function *HalfAdd* is a specification of a primitive component. The composition of the primitive components is described by **macro** statements which define more complex objects in terms of other *macros* and primitive **functions**. ELLA programs may use conditional and case statements to describe alternative choice and action selection. Recursion may also be used within an ELLA program to reduce the size of the description. This technique is very powerful, and derives from the more advanced programming languages. For a more detailed description of recursion and its use as a programming tool, see Chapter 13 of this book. Repetitive statements can also be used within ELLA descriptions.

A particularly interesting feature of the language is the **type** statement which permits new types to be created. Composite types may also be created out of previously defined types, and operators exist for accessing different parts of signals embedded in complex type definitions. This typing mechanism ensures that inputs to components are not inadvertently confused. This is a problem that MODEL and FIRST do not handle. They rely on the designer of the circuit providing the appropriate number of connections to particular components.

The **export** mechanism is also interesting as it allows components to be explicitly exported to the outside world, while marking the actual implementation as private. This permits another ELLA designer to use a defined macro, which may be found in a design library, without knowing how it has been implemented. This prevents the designer making unrealistic assumptions about parts of his design. If the design of that component changes, thus invalidating his assumption, he would need to alter possibly all of his design. By effectively preventing him access to the implementation of another macro, the designer is forced to rely just upon the interface to that component and its specification which should be independent of the actual implementation. This technique is the hardware equivalent of the 'abstract data type' mechanism [7] developed for programmers who are designing large software systems.

12.5   STRICT: Strongly Typed Recursive Integrated Circuits

STRICT [8] is the result of a collaborative project between the Computing Laboratory and the Department of Electrical and Electrical Engineering at the University of Newcastle upon Tyne. It has been designed as an integral part of a much wider project to develop software based VLSI design tools. As such, the language is a first attempt to define a notation that will be used to describe designs which might contain over a million gates.

The languages described so far have required that the designer be responsible for breaking the overall design into smaller, simpler sub-designs. In addition, he has been responsible for ensuring that this decomposition has been done correctly, and that the resulting implemented system meets the specification that was initially provided.

However, concern is growing that the designer will be unable to perform these checks manually because of the problems of complexity posed by designing with over a million gates. In effect, he will be totally overwhelmed by the details that the design system will encourage him to generate.

One of the main aims behind the design of STRICT has been the tackling of the specification and consistency problem. Before a designer starts to implement a system, he will be required to provide an abstract specification of what the system is supposed to do. At all stages of the subsequent decomposition, he will be able to check that his initial specification is still being met. If for some reason it is not, then he has the opportunity to alter either his implementation or initial specification. In the short term, this checking will be performed by a simulator, but in the longer term, more formal verification techniques will be supported. Ultimately, it is hoped that a designer, having provided his initial specification, will just compile it, allowing the design system to transform it into a viable chip. Such ideas are however, a long way off at present.

The language is designed for fully custom integrated circuit design, and an integrated design environment is envisaged. This will include a language compiler (with an associated syntax/graphics directed editor), simulator, layout system and other tools.

The designer is not responsible for specifying which bonding pads are required, or for optimally placing them. STRICT is designed to be a fully automatic design system, allowing the designer to concentrate upon designing the required circuit, but it is acknowledged that in the short term, certain pragmats will have to be supplied to the design system through the high-level language for realistic layouts to be produced.

A STRICT design is a hierarchy of blocks, where each block represents a functional component of the system. Each component will transform its inputs into other defined outputs. Each component (or BLOCK) is constructed from two parts:

— a *specification*:   a description of the interface to the outside world and a declaration of the blocks intended function;
— an *implementation*:   a description of how the specification may be realized structurally, in terms of other, probably simpler blocks.

Strong typing, as is found in programming languages such as Pascal, is used extensively to enable checks to be made on the consistency of connections between blocks. User-defined types are also supported, the designer being responsible for defining the values they may take, and in addition, for interface types (that is, types that are used to connect blocks together) the representation of the values in terms of **wires** and a mapping from the wires to the values.

As an example of the STRICT language the following is a description of a shift register chip.

```
build
  { instance
       reg : SRreg(5)
    using
       reg(SRin, phi1, phi2)
    make
       SRout ::= reg.output
  }
  given
     block SRreg (size : integer)
     having (input@W : wire
              clk1@N, clk2@N : clock(5,5)):
              (output@E : wire)
```

```
                    intended behaviour
                    whenever
                        change(input):
                            within cycle(clk1) * size
                        set
                            output = input
                    use structure
                    (size==1):{inherit
                            srcell
                        instance
                            src:srcell
                        using
                            src(input, clk1,clk2)
                        make
                            output::= src.output
                    }
                    (size>1):{ inherit
                            srcell
                        instance
                            src:srcell
                            shortreg:SRreg(size-1)
                        place
                            src; shortreg
                        using
                            src(input,clk1,clk2)
                            shortreg(src.output, clk1,clk2)
                        make
                            output ::= shortreg.output
                    }
        end
```

The design starts by requesting an instance of a particular block, in this case an *SRreg*. Associated with this block is a name. This block then has names associated with the inputs and outputs. The design system, from this initial request, will be responsible for determining the appropriate number of pads required including power and ground.

Then follows the declaration of the block *SRreg*. It starts with details about its interface to the outside world. The parameter *size* is called a generic parameter; it enables a variety of *SRreg*s to be described, all defined by *size*. The input and output interfaces follow which identify the local names of the interfaces, their types (which in this instance include a pre-defined type called 'clock' which has parameters defining its rise and fall time), and a pragmat which places the interfaces on particular sides of the block. If this pragmat is not provided, the design system can choose where to place them itself.

The specification of the block then follows. It describes what happens when a change is observed on the input, and how this affects the result obtained on the output. The predefined operators *change* and *cycle* are used in this context.

Finally the implementation follows. There are two alternatives, defined by the generic parameter size. The first simply inherits another block called *srcell* and uses it. The second inherits *srcell* and uses it in conjunction with a slightly shorter *SRreg*. Notice that the implementation of the shift register is expressed declaratively. That is, inputs are implicitly connected to outputs, unlike MODEL and FIRST. Connections are made by affectively calling each instanced block with its input parameters, which may be, in turn, the outputs of other instanced blocks, or the inputs of the block being implemented. The output of the block being specified is described in terms of the outputs of other instanced blocks. The **place** statement is another pragmat placed by the designer to suggest to the design system how to arrange the instanced blocks relative to each other. In this example, they are to be placed next to each other. The other option is to place one above the other. If no placement is suggested, the design system determines a suitable one.

The design environment for STRICT is currently being implemented, with particular attention being concentrated upon the layout and simulation sub-systems. In addition, primitive design libraries to support a variety of technologies are also being designed.

12.6   Summary

The concept of a silicon compiler is slowly becoming more widely accepted. Few general purpose systems are as yet available, but a number of special purpose compilers are in use. A number of problems remain to be solved however, and two distinct views currently exist.

One view maintains that chip layout is very similar to the problem of compiling a program and producing machine code. If general purpose silicon compilers were available, the effort currently expended on design would be reduced by a factor of approximately 20. By using a compiler, circuits stand more chance of being designed correctly in terms of their functional specifications. As a consequence, the amount of design rule checking and simulation that would be required to verify a design would drop significantly. At the present time the compilers that do exist, and the languages that are input to them are very simple, but, as experience is gained with them, they will improve until ultimately they will match and surpass the traditional techniques, and in addition will bring additional benefits such as the guarantee that the silicon produced is correct.

However, the other view maintains that chip design is a two-dimensional problem, unlike software compilation which is one-dimensional. Algorithms for automatic routing and placement will never match those of a human designer because of their complexity, and consequently, chip performance, measured in speed and area used, will be impaired by automatic techniques. The physical realities of producing manufactuarable integrated circuits are too complex for the existence of a silicon compiler to affect.

But is this view justified? Are these not the same points that were made in the early 1960s when programming language compilers were first designed? Well, only time will tell.

> When FORTRAN was originally implemented, it gave relatively poor results in terms of code, space and speed. Once we understood it better — got it refined — most people came to realise that for large programs, a good global optimising FORTRAN compiler will generate better code than hand crafted code. That's my desire for a silicon compiler.
>
> *C. Rupp, Digital Equipment Corp.*

References

1. Mead, C. and Conway, L. *Introduction to VLSI Systems*. Addison-Wesley (1980).
2. Locanthi, B. *LAP: A SIMULA Package for IC Layout*, Caltech Display File No. 1862 (1978).
3. Gray, J.P. *et al*. Designing gate arrays using a silicon compiler. *Proc. 19th Design Automation Conference*. Las Vegas (1982).
4. Dahl, O.J., Hoare, C.A.R., and Dijkstra, E.W. *Structured Programming*. Academic Press (1972).
5. Bergmann, N. *A Case Study of the F.I.R.S.T. Silicon Compiler*. University of Edinburgh, Dept of Computer Science, Internal Report, CSR-159-84 (1984).
6. Morison, J.D. Peeling, N.E., and Thorp, T.L. Specification: a use for HDL's (to be published).
7. Guttag, J. Abstract Data Types and the Development of Data Structures. *CAM*, **20**(6), 1977.
8. Campbell, R.C., Koelmans, A.M. and McLauchlan, M.R. STRICT: a design language for Strongly Typed Recursive Integrated Circuits. *IEE Proceedings*, **132** (2), Pts E and I, 1985.

13　Functional languages

13.1　Introduction

So far in this book, it has been assumed that the reader has a basic knowledge of a traditional programming language such as FORTRAN, Pascal, or Ada. Collectively such languages are known as *imperative languages*. They have been used to implement most of the software written over the last 25 years. If a program is to be written, then these languages are the first choice.

Historically, such languages can be classed as 'third generation' languages, as compared to 'first generation' languages which encompass machine codes, and 'second generation' languages which encompass assembly languages.

To a certain extent, all these languages perform the same task. They endeavour to describe how the physical attributes of a particular machine (that is, registers, ALU's, memory cells, etc.) may be used in a particular way to provide the desired procedure or program, as specified by a particular specification. The difference between the different 'generations' is the degree of visibility of a particular piece of hardware, and how easy the resulting algorithm, when expressed in a particular language, is to understand by a human reader. Programs written in first generation languages are notoriously difficult to understand and debug, particularly when compared to a well-written program in a third generation language.

One of the main factors that has influenced the design of programming languages over the last few years has been the problem of providing a sufficiently rich set of language primitives allowing programs to be written in terms of the objects and operations of the problem domain, while allowing the resulting program to be executed as efficiently as possible on the actual hardware. One only has to look at the documentation provided for languages such as PL/1 and Ada to see how complicated they are.

As a consequence, trade-offs have to be made to allow such languages to be implemented satisfactorily, and it is the programmer's interface that usually suffers. As a result, the writing of an imperative program is a difficult process as it is the responsibility of the programmer to map his high-level abstractions to the language primitives, which at best are very simple.

Imperative programs are oriented very much towards the execution of successive statements in a defined sequence. This is because the design of the language has been heavily influenced by the architecture of the computer upon which the program will ultimately be executed. This architecture, which is described as von Neumann after the man who pioneered it, is very simple and has been used successfully for over thirty years.[1]

A von Neumann computer, in its simplest form, has three components. They are the central processing unit (CPU), the memory and a data bus which links the first two together. In order for the computer to perform any calculation, the values must be brought from the memory to the CPU, via the data bus. Consequently, the speed with which this data bus can transfer data heavily influences the overall execution speed of the computer as a whole.

To make efficient use of this architecture it must be possible to influence directly the movement of data between the memory and CPU. Consequently, imperative languages have the following characteristics.

— Programs manipulate *variables*, that is, named locations within the memory in which data (either simple, i.e. integer, logical, etc., or compound, i.e. array, record, file, etc.), can be stored. It is very important for the program to look in the right variable for particular pieces of information, and the more variables there are, the more difficult this becomes.

— A program's unit of work is a *statement*, and by combining the action of a number of them together, the desired result for the whole program may be achieved.

— All programs use *assignment statements* to specify which values are to be stored in which variables for later use. In general, the assignment statement is very low level. It is rare to find a language where the contents of entire arrays may be assigned from one variable to another in one statement. It is more usual to do it one element at a time.

— Programs of any level of sophistication, in order to accomplish their task, must execute a sequence of statements *repeatedly*. This is a direct consequence of machine instructions being stored in memory.

In order to write an imperative program, it is therefore necessary to describe 'how' the language may be used to generate the necessary results. This involves breaking the program down into a number of smaller sections, which may then be each treated as programs in their own right. This results in the program having to execute repeatedly a number of step by step computations of low-level values, with assignment of these values to appropriate memory locations. To determine the actual result of an imperative program requires that it be *executed* — a dynamic process.

At present, hardware costs are dropping dramatically, while software costs are rising. Computers are getting bigger and faster. But, the programs that run upon these faster machines are unable to benefit, because of the limitations of the databus connecting the memory to the CPU. It has become a bottleneck, reducing the execution speed of the machine as a whole.

However, other classes of Programming Languages do exist, which do not rely on the von Neumann architecture. Two classes of particular interest are *Logic* [2] and *Functional* (or *Applicative*) [3] languages. The remainder of this chapter will introduce to the reader the basic concepts of Functional Languages, and will identify the advantages that they have over Imperative Languages.

13.2 Functional languages

Functional Languages are based upon the mathematical idea of a function. A functional programmer writes his program in terms of the objects he wishes to manipulate. He is not involved then in describing those objects in terms of simpler ones (as does his imperative colleague) because the data structures provided by the language are also very abstract. They are consequently very general purpose and can be adapted to different environments very easily. The result of a functional program is obtained by *evaluating* an expression — a static process.

Therefore, programs that can be long and difficult to write in conventional languages are often shorter and clearer to write in functional form. They are also written in much shorter, simpler, well defined sections which require less debugging and lead quite naturally to the idea of 'correctness by construction'.

But there are currently disadvantages. Current implementation of functional languages on von Neumann computers are, in general, very inefficient in their use of hardware. Consequently, they are not as yet used widely, though research into alternative computer architectures will change this. As soon as it is possible to execute a functional program quickly and more efficiently than at present, they will provide a viable alternative to imperative languages, and the days of languages like FORTRAN will be numbered.

> . . . the next revolution in programming will take place only when both of the following requirements have been met.
> (a) a new kind of programming language, far more powerful than those of today, has been developed, and
> (b) a technique has been found for executing its programs at not much greater cost than that of today's programs.
>
> *John Backus, ACM Sigplan 1978*
> *History of Programming Language Conference*
> *Sigplan Notices 138 (August 1978).*

13.2.1 BASIC CONCEPTS

A function is a rule for mapping (or associating) members of one set (the *domain*) to those of another (the *range*). Functions may be described in a variety of ways. One method might enumerate all the possible mappings that are available. For example, the function mapping particular married couples to their children might be described as follows:

John and Mary Smith	→	Tim, Mary, Joanne
Michael and Julie Jones	→	Colin, Steven
Paul and Tracy Simpson	→	Alison
domain	function	range

The names of the husbands and wives, as pairs, form the domain set, while the list of the children in the family form the range set. For a large domain set, this method of defining the function is both tedious and error prone.

Another approach is therefore to describe formal rules which govern the mapping of the domain set (the inputs) to the range set (the outputs). Such rules will describe a much larger set of mappings than is possible by direct enumeration. This is the principle behind functional programming. For example, the function increment, which adds one to its input might be defined as follows.

$$increment(x:integer) ::= x + 1$$

It is assumed that the addition operation maps to the set of integers. This general purpose function will map any integer to another and describes the mapping from a very large (infinite) domain set to a correspondingly large range set.

Having *defined* a function, it may be *applied* to particular elements of the domain set. For example,

increment(3)
increment(5)

The application yields (or results in, or returns) the associated element in the range set. For example,

increment(3)   yields   4
increment(5)   yields   6

An important advantage of the functional approach to programming, and one which will significantly affect the way in which such languages are implemented in the future, is that the result of a function application, or indeed, the value of any expression in a functional program, is determined solely by the values of its constituent parts. So, provided the context remains the same for both occurrences, the value of two identical expressions remains the same for both occurrences. This is not true in an imperative language. For example the function increment, defined earlier, when applied to the value 2, will always yield the answer 3, regardless of the context. However, if the function is defined in an imperative language, the result may be

function *increment(x:integer):interger*;
increment := *x* + 1 * *a*;

When it is applied to the value 2, the result depends upon the global variable '*a*'. In a functional language, no global variables are allowed, so such a dependency is not allowed. Imperative languages are not as strict, and consequently, such dependencies do arise and make programs much more difficult to understand.

A reliable functional program should only define and use *total* functions. That is, functions which always return a value in the range set for every value in the domain set. In contrast, *partial* functions only return values in the range set for some of the values in the domain set. The remainder are undefined. Another restriction on a functional language is that 'computation by side effect' is not permitted. This is related to the earlier point about the absence of global variables. As a consequence, the following imperative program could not be translated directly into its functional equivalent, without a certain amount of rearrangement.

```
function max(x,y:integer):integer;
begin
  if x:= y  then max := x
            else max := y;
    maxsum := maxsum + max
end;
```

The assignment to *maxsum*, a global variable to the function *max*, is a side effect of the execution of the function. Language features that permit computation by side effect are provided to permit efficient use of the machine.

Another important difference between imperative and functional languages is that a functional language should be as simple as possible. It will provide a small but very powerful set of primitive operations, out of which more complicated operations may be constructed. The data structures it provides must also be simple in design, yet powerful in concept. It should be able to model all possible data structures that might be required.

Therefore, a functional language can be shown to have the following four components.

(1) a set of data objects — to be manipulated by the program;
(2) a set of primitive functions — providing a set of basic building blocks;
(3) a set of functional forms — a way to construct new building blocks;
(4) the application operation — a request for the result.

13.3   Lispkit Lisp [3] — a particular language

The Lispkit Lisp language is a purely functional derivative of the programming language Lisp 1.5 and was developed by Henderson while at the Universities of Newcastle upon Tyne, Oxford and Stirling. It has gone through a number of revisions, and is currently available for a number of different machines. It comes complete with its own design environment, which is also written in Lispkit Lisp. The version shown here is a subset providing sufficient facilities to show how it may be used. Further details may be found in the references.

The language has the following four components.

13.3.1   DATA OBJECTS

Lispkit Lisp manipulates symbolic expressions (also known as S-expressions or lists). S-expressions are built from atoms which are indivisible objects, either symbolic or numeric, and parentheses. They are defined as follows:

(1) An atom is an S-expression.
(2) A sequence of S-expressions enclosed in parentheses is an S-expression.

So, for example, the following are all S-expressions.

Hello
(This is 1984)
((This car) which (is blue (and small))(is mine))

13.3.2 PRIMITIVE FUNCTIONS

There are two forms of primitive function available. Functions in the first category are responsible for building and splitting S-expressions. Those in the second handle the basic predicates and arithmetic operations that the language needs to make it usable.

There are three list-manipulating functions.

$head(x)$ selects the first member of the list x.

$tail(x)$ selects the lists which results from omitting the first member of x.

$join(x,y)$ results in a list with x added as the first member of the list y.

NIL returns a special list which has no members, and can be regarded as the empty list.

The following examples show how these functions are used.

x	$head(x)$	$tail(x)$
(1 2 3)	1	(2 3)
((a b)c (d e))	(a b)	(c (d e))

x	y	$join(x,y)$
a	(b c)	(a b c)
(1 2)	(3 4)	((1 2) 3 4)

There are number of predicates and arithmetic operations in the language, most of which will be familiar. One that will not be is $atom(x)$. It returns the value true if x is an atom, and false otherwise. There are also predicates to compare the relationship between S-expressions. They are defined only if at least one of the S-expressions is atomic. They are

$$< , <= , = , >= , >$$

The inequalities may only be applied to numeric atoms. Numeric atoms are just integers. Most other forms could be simulated by defining the appropriate functions and data structures. The following integer operations are implemented.

$+ , - , {}^{*},$ **div** , **rem**

13.3.3 FUNCTIONAL FORMS

A number are provided within the language. Two will be described: a conditional expression and a mechanism for defining new functions. A third will be introduced in the next sction when it is needed.

The conditional form looks as follows:

if x **then** y **else** z

Depending upon the value of x, which is assumed to be of type Boolean, evaluate y or z. If x is true, then evaluate y, otherwise evaluate z. Unlike Pascal, there is no short form (where the **else** part is omitted). That would allow the definition of partial functions.

To define a new function requires specifying a name and providing the appropriate formal arguments, each identified with a suitable identifier.

$$f(x1,x2,x3, \ldots ,xn) ::= e \qquad n>=0$$

f introduces the name of the function. It can have any number of arguments, all with different names. The arguments are of no particular type, though they will be S-expressions. It is the programmer's responsibility to pass arguments of the appropriate type and structure to a particular function. This is no problem, provided the programmer chooses suitable identifiers for the arguments. The function *f* is defined to be the result of evaluating the expression *e*, in which the arguments, *x1*, . . . ,*xn* are assumed to appear.

A function need not just be defined to accept S-expressions as arguments. Functions may also be passed as arguments. In this way, special purpose functions may be created from general purpose functions. For example, a list sorting function that sorts into ascending order might be defined in terms of a general purpose sorting function, where the ranking to be applied is supplied by an argument which is also a function. Similarly, a function need not only yield a result in the form of an S-expression. Instead, a function might be returned as the result, which could be applied at a later date to the appropriate arguments. These are examples of what are termed *higher-order functions*. Such features make functional languages very powerful.

13.3.4 APPLICATION OPERATION

Finally, a mechanism is needed to enable arguments to be applied to previously defined functions.

$$f(exp1,exp2,exp3, \ldots ,expn) \qquad n>=0$$

The function, called *f*, is applied to its arguments *exp1*, . . . ,expn. Semantically, the result of the function application is determined as follows. The value of each expression passed as an argument is substituted into the definition of the function at the points indicated by the corresponding formal argument. The resulting expression is then evaluated and the result returned. The evaluation of the expression may cause other functions to be applied to their arguments.

There are no iterative constructs in most functional languages. Instead, *recursion* is used. This involves a function's definition referencing itself with a slightly different set of actual arguments, thus causing another evaluation of that function. In addition to the recursive call, there must be some additional code which describes how the recursion is to terminate.

The example that follows will show how the language just defined can be used to write useful programs.

13.4 An example

To demonstrate how effective a functional language can be in describing a complicated problem succinctly, consider the task of writing a simulator for the *n*-bit multiplier [4] which is shown in Fig. 13.1. The interested reader might consider carrying out the same task in an imperative language, and comparing the resulting program with what follows.

The diagram shows it to be composed of three basic components: a *multiplier*, a *parallel full-adder* and a *carry propagate adder*.

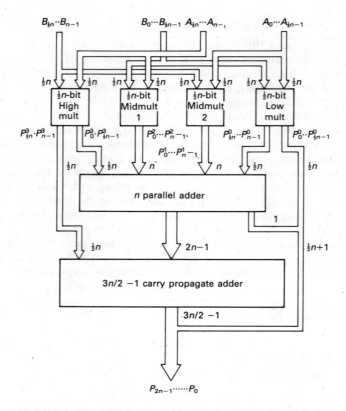

Fig. 13.1   Block diagram of an n-bit multiplier.

In providing a program to simulate this structure the following decisions will be made. Each component will be defined at two levels. The higher level describes what size of input and output the component operates upon, in terms of the number of bits. For example, an n-bit multiplier multiplies n-bit inputs and produces $2n$-bit outputs. The lower level identifies the actual inputs to the component. By splitting the definition in this way, it is possible to describe a general purpose component which, when provided with arguments for the higher level, instances a particular component. This in turn may be applied to a number of different physical inputs. It is felt that this is clearer than mixing these two distinctly different types of argument at the same level. To be able to perform this multi-level definition, higher-order functions will be used. It should be obvious when they are being used and no further explanation will be given here. The interested reader should investigate the references further.

Concentrating initially upon the multiplier, it can be defined in terms of the number of bits that make up each multiplicand, which is assumed to be a power of 2, and in terms of its two inputs, a and b. Functions may return only one result, an S-expression, and that is all that is needed here. Therefore the overall description of the multiplier, as suggested by Fig. 13.1, may now be given.

$$multiplier(n)(a,b) ::=$$
$$\text{if } n <= 2 \text{ then}$$
$$a * b$$
$$\text{else}$$
$$leastsighalf(n)(lowmult) +$$
$$shiftleft(n \text{ div } 2)(sum) +$$
$$shiftleft(n \text{ div } 2) + 1$$
$$(CPadd(cin, remainder,$$
$$mostsighalf(n)(highmult))$$

The inputs, *a* and *b*, are assumed to be numbers (i.e. integers). However, it is also assumed that the program may only multiply the two inputs directly when they may be represented by two-bit patterns, hence the first 'arm' of the conditional expression. This is the non-recursive part of the function and stops the recursive calls on 'multiplier'. The other 'arm' of the conditional expression describes how the result may be obtained from the inputs *a* and *b* when they are represented by larger bit patterns. This is in terms of the other components indicated in the Fig. 13.1. To distinguish between the four different multipliers that are required, they are given the names *lowmult*, *midmult1*, *midmult2* and *highmult*. Other identifiers also appear in the above description and at present are undefined. The functions *leastsighalf*, *mostsighalf* and *shiftleft* are general purpose, programmer-defined functions that correspond to the bus splitting and joining operations shown in the diagram. For example, *mostsighalf* is defined as follows:

$$mostsighalf(n)(x) ::= x \text{ div } 2^{**}(n \text{ div } 2)$$

Note that the operation $2^{**}Y$ (*raise to the power of*) is not a primitive of the language, but must be defined by the programmer. *Leastsighalf* and *shiftleft* can be defined similarly.

A functional programming system, such as Lispkit Lisp, allows users to define 'libraries' of useful, general purpose functions, each of which is tailored to specific application areas and will be used over and over again in different programs. The programmer is therefore capable of tailoring his functional language to his own particular area of interest, and he is not cluttered by primitives which are of no use to him. Compare this approach with languages such as PL/1 and Ada.

Lowmult and *highmult*, as stated previously, are the identifiers for the smaller multipliers. *Lowmult* is responsible for multiplying the least significant halves of the inputs, while *highmult* multiplies the most significant halves. *Midmult1* and *midmult2* are responsible for performing the other two multiplications. They are defined as follows.

$$lowmult \quad = multiplier(n \text{ div } 2)(leastsighalf(n)(a),$$
$$leastsighalf(n)(b))$$
$$midmult1 = multiplier(n \text{ div } 2)(mostsighalf(n)(a),$$
$$leastsighalf(n)(b))$$
$$midmult2 = multiplier(n \text{ div } 2)(leastsighalf(n)(a),$$
$$mostsighalf(n)(b)$$
$$highmult \quad = multiplier(n \text{ div } 2)(mostsighalf(n)(a),$$
$$mostsighalf(n)(b))$$

These equations are not new function definitions, but logical renamings, hence the use of the '=' symbol. Semantically, every instance of one of these identifiers may be replaced with the corresponding expression.

Sum, remainder and *cin* are outputs of the parallel full-adder component, and are derived from its single result. The result of the parallel full-adder is *n* pairs of two bits, a sum and carry for each of the corresponding input bits. *Sum* is therefore the least significant sum bit, *cin* the least significant carry bit, and *remainder* is the rest of the result. This can be expressed as follows.

$$
\begin{aligned}
sum &= head(head(Paraddout)) \\
cin &= tail(head(Paraddout)) \\
remainder &= tail(Paraddout) \\
Paraddout &= \\
&\quad reverse(Paraadd(n)(shiftleft(n \textbf{ div } 2) (leastsighalf(n)(highmult)), \\
&\qquad\qquad\qquad midmult1, \\
&\qquad\qquad\qquad midmult2, \\
&\qquad\qquad\qquad mostsighalf(n)(lowmult))
\end{aligned}
$$

A limitation of Lispkit Lisp is that it constructs and selects only from the left end of a list, so the programmer-defined function *reverse* is used to reverse the resulting list produced by the parallel full-adder.

Only two identifiers remain to be defined, *CPadd* and *Paraadd*, which correspond to the parallel full-adder and carry-propagate adder.

The parallel full-adders task is to take the four inputs, and simultaneously to add the corresponding bits of each input together, producing a sum and carry bit for each. The resulting *n* pairs of sum and carry bits are returned as the result.

```
Paraadd(n)(mcand1,mcand2,mcand3,mcand4) ::=
  if n <= 1 then
    join(join(mcandsum rem 2, mcandsum div 2), NIL)
  else
    append(Paraadd(n−1)(mcand1 div 2,
                        mcand2 div 2,
                        mcand3 div 2,
                        mcand4 div 2),
    join(join(rmcandsum rem 2,
             rmcandsum div 2),
        NIL))
  whererec
    mcandsum = mcand1 + mcand2 + mcand3 + mcand4
    rmcandsum = rmcand1 + rmcand2 + rmcand3 + rmcand4
    rmcand1 = mcand1 rem 2
    rmcand2 = mcand2 rem 2
    rmcand3 = mcand2 rem 2
    rmcand4 = mcand4 rem 2
```

The function *append* takes two lists and produces as a result a single list, with all the items in the first list followed by the items in the second list. The language construct **whererec** allows local logical renamings to be associated with a particular expression. Hence, within the confines of the conditional form, the identifiers defined by the **whererec** may be used. This is another example of a functional form (see Section 13.3.3).

Finally, the carry-propagate adder takes the $n-1$ sum and carry bit pairs, plus the least significant carry bit, and the result of multiplying the most significant halves of the original inputs, and adds them together.

```
CPadd(cin,bitpairs,multsighalf) ::=
    if null(bitpairs) then
        cin + multsighalf
    else
        cin + sumbit(head(bitpairs))+
          2 * CPadd(carrybit(head(bitpairs)),
                    tail(bitpairs),
                    multsighalf)
    where
        sumbit(pair)  ::= head(pair)
        carrybit(pair) ::= tail(pair)
```

Null(*a*) is a predicate which yields true if *a* is the empty list, that is *NIL*, and false otherwise.

It only remains now to check the program, by applying the function multiplier to some suitable arguments:

multiplier(4)(15,12)

The result obtained should be 180.

13.5 Summary

This chapter has shown a distinctly different style of programming to the one that is by tradition understood. The interest shown in the computing science community for it is still increasing, and there are several reasons for this. Some are concerned about the complexity of current traditional languages, and see no universal imperative language solving the problem. Others, concerned about the problems of explicitly identifying parallelism, feel that functional languages offer hope, as no restrictions are placed upon how a program may be executed. Parallelism can be handled with no extra information being provided by the programmer. Yet more, worried about the basic complexity of programming, and the problems of thinking up suitable algorithms, prefer to concentrate their attentions on writing functional specifications of what they would like their program to do, and hope that, ultimately, a program transformation system will transform their abstract specification into a runnable program. All this may become possible with functional languages; it will certainly not be possible with imperative language.

The computing science community have been investigating these problems for a number of years, and now, with the advent of VLSI, the silicon designer is beginning to suffer from similar problems. Very complicated 'imperative languages' which specify how a circuit should be constructed in great detail, a step at a time, are very much in evidence. Others try to capture the concepts of concurrency in hardware, and so far, do not do so very elegantly. Large designs (that is, more than five hundred thousand gates) will need to provide initial specifications of what is wanted and then, once fabricated, will need to check that the specification has been met. As the designs get bigger this capability will not be provided by traditional simulators. Formal verification of some other kind will need to be employed, which means that current languages will need to be re-designed to encompass formal techniques. By adopting the functional style now, many of these problems could be circumvented. In the long term, it may be even possible to provide a specification of a piece of hardware at the top level, which may then be transformed automatically (with the help of an expert system) into an actual piece of hardware. No simulation or verification would be necessary as the transformation would guarantee 'correctness by construction'.

Lispkit Lisp is based on the programming language Lisp 1.5, which has its origins in the early 1960s, and could be regarded by some as too simple to be effective. But as a language to introduce the techniques of functional programming, and for experimenting with it, it is invaluable. Other languages also exist, such as ML [5], KRV [6] and FP [1]. They are currently being used in a variety of application areas, such as theorem proving [7], VLSI design [8], expert systems [9] and operating systems design [10].

With the arrival of VLSI, the possibility of non-von Neumann architectures of hundreds or even thousands of relatively simple processors has become a reality. Once the problems of interconnecting them is solved satisfactorily, and thus allows efficient execution of such programs, enormous advances in the application areas that may be tackled will be made.

References

1. Backus, J. Can Programming be liberated from the von Neumann Style? A Functional Style and its Algebra of Programs. *CACM* **21**(8) (1978).
2. Kowalski, R. Predicate LOgic as a Programming Language. *Proc. IFIP-74*, North-Holland (1974).
3. Henderson, P. *Functional Programming: Application and Implementation*. Prentice-Hall, International Series in Computer Science (1980).
4. Yung, H.C. and Allen, C.R. An optimised hierarchical multiplier. *Proc. IEE(G) Circuits and Systems* (1983).
5. Damas, L. and Milner, R. Principal type-schemes for functional programs. *Proc. 9th Symposium on Principles of Programming Languages* (1982).
6. Turner, D.A. Recursive equations as a programming language. In *Functional Programming and its Applications*, edited by J. Darlington, P. Henderson, and D.A. Turner. Cambridge University Press (1981).
7. Boyer, R.S. and Strother-Moore, J. *A Computational Logic*. ACM Monograph Series, Academic Press (1979).
8. Sheeran, M. *muFP, an Algebraic VLSI Design Language*. Internal Report, Oxford University Computing Laboratory, Programming Research Group (1983).
9. Henderson, P., Jones, G.A., and Jones, S.B. *The Lispkit Manual*. Technical Monograph PRG-32(1), Programming Research Group, Oxford University (1983).
10. Henderson, P. Purely functional operating systems. In *Functional Programming and its Applications*, edited by J. Darlington, P. Henderson and D.A. Turner, Cambridge University Press (1981).

Index